THE TROUBLED BED

OTHER BOOKS BY THE AUTHOR

A MINNESOTA DOCTOR'S HOME REMEDIES
FOR COMMON AND UNCOMMON AILMENTS

THE MARRIAGE ART

NEW APPROACHES TO SEX IN MARRIAGE

The Troubled Bed

THE OBSTACLES TO SEXUAL HAPPINESS IN
MARRIAGE—AND WHAT YOU CAN DO ABOUT THEM

by John E. Eichenlaub, M.D.

DELACORTE PRESS/NEW YORK, N.Y.

To my patients,
from the ashes of whose miseries
this book took root

Contents

	Introduction	xi
1.	FAILURE?	1
2.	PREPARATION FOR INTERCOURSE	16
3.	SEX VERSUS LOVE	33
4.	ORGASM BY PLAY ONLY	44
5.	THE FRIGID WOMAN	58
6.	POTENCY FEARS	74
7.	SEX AND THE PILL	90
8.	SEX AND THE MENOPAUSE	105
9.	INFIDELITY	121
10.	QUESTIONS OF CONSCIENCE	134
11.	IDENTITY CONFLICTS	154
	Index	167

Introduction

After my book *The Marriage Art* became popular, many couples with sexual problems were sent to me. Some of their difficulties were unique, some were unalterable, but a great many fell into certain patterns and yielded to fairly simple measures. And it is from their experiences that *The Troubled Bed* is drawn.

My patients' confidences have to be kept, of course, so the case reports set forth here are *not* word-for-word transcriptions of real consultations. Each report is actually an amalgam of several cases, authentic, however, as a description of a real and common problem, the responses to it, and the means of solving it.

The picture you will get of each common sexual difficulty should help in several ways. If you have suffered similar difficulties, you may well find that the measures which helped these couples will also help *you*. The techniques, altered values or attitudes, and other elements which proved helpful to my clients are spelled out in detail. You can use them as home remedies with every hopeful expectation.

You may also derive more subtle benefits from this book. Couples often learn to understand each other's viewpoints, and perhaps work out compromise positions on many matters, through discussion of someone else's situation. If third person discourse leads into an open, compassionate, and constructive discussion of those elements of your own sex life which can be improved—and every couple has some—you will almost certainly improve your mutual understanding and will quite probably improve your practices. Even if book-inspired conversations never touch on your own specific feelings, attitudes, or desires, the better understanding produced by couple communication about sex may well prove salutary.

Improved general understanding may help you, too. Perhaps no man ever understands a woman completely, and no woman a man, but an insight into the sexual yearnings, frustrations, doubts, hesitations, and fears of the other sex adds depth to your appreciation. So does an understanding of members of your own sex whose problems are different, perhaps opposite, from your own. The assertive male will never fully understand the self-effacing one, and the frustrated, constantly yearning "sexpot" will never fully understand the inhibited, unresponsive "old-maid-though-married," but perhaps each can better appreciate the other by reading a compassionate account of their separate sexual struggles.

Hopefully, this book has preventive value, too. If the next generation can be induced to attach to the sexual element of marriage the same values of total social acceptance and eager anticipation which the last generation quite properly has linked with romantic love, and to leach out the false modesty and unjustified shame which so often mar sexual fulfillment today, a vast cohesive force will be added to the modern family.

Sex is a vital drive, and one about which most people have little true knowledge. In fact, almost all scientific work in this field is really pioneering. Almost no medical schools have been teaching the management of couple sex problems, or even the normal functioning of the various glands and organs during intercourse, for long enough that their programs can be considered to be firmly established. The study of couple dynamics is so new that there isn't even a word for it: "psychology" studies the interaction of the individual with his environment, "sociology" the interaction of various groups, but the mechanisms by which a loving couple interact are distinctly different from either of these and have no "ology" to fit them.

Although all of the techniques and approaches discussed in this book thus have an experimental element, I can assure you that those which may seem the most shocking or unusual have been used and accepted rather widely by informed couple counselors. Even my urbane editors felt some dismay at reading how I explain sexual anatomy and technique by alternately exposing husband and wife to each other, right down to the most remote portion of the genitals. A few years ago this idea would have shocked me, too, and I'll admit to considerable trepidation before I first tried it. But the people who had reported this technique at a national conference were perfectly reputable, a number of the other conferees had used the method with success, and so I decided to try it with a particularly suitable couple. The results were so favorable and the emotional upheaval so slight that I've used this method earlier and earlier in my counseling routine, and with less and less limitation in selection of couples. While I still don't go through this program with every client, recently the average has been close to nine out of ten, and a follow-up survey almost always shows that the couples rate this experience as most helpful.

Two other points about the reported cases deserve comment. First, I have obviously selected cases which respond best to simple measures so that the types of insight and knowledge you can gain from reading about them will do the most good. The percentage of clients reported as being dramatically helped is thus substantially higher than my own (or anyone else's) across-the-board average.

Second, many of these cases have necessarily been sharply condensed. When a couple requires in-depth counseling, the process by which they make progress is a far from steady one. There's a big breakthrough to a new level, and everybody—husband, wife, and counselor—gets a complete picture of the situation, which then holds up for a variable length of time (from a few seconds to months). During this period, there are long dreary stretches of squabbling or discourse before another great breakthrough occurs. There are perhaps six or eight such revisions of the image before we get to the picture from which resolution of the difficulty comes—and even then we may be dealing with the difficulties on a symbolic level rather than at their core. In some of the actual cases upon which this book is based, the significant moments reported as arising in one or two interviews might be strung out over six months; very few of the actual cases involving realigned couple relations or deep emotional insights involved less than fifteen or twenty conferences. So please don't expect any counselor to match the time record established in these reports.

It is perhaps a profound conceit to claim authenticity for purposely disguised cases, to claim established value for admittedly experimental techniques, to claim broad applicability for a far from random selection of cases, and to claim to convey insights through vastly abbreviated case accounts. However, these dilemmas are intrinsic to writing in a taboo-laden field. As I turn this manuscript over to the printer, I know that my colleagues are going to damn some of my case reports as being too pat, too cut-and-dried, too quick in reaching the point. I know that some of my readers are going to damn their present or future counselors for being too vague, too passive, too slow in giving concrete aid. The misunderstanding in both cases will be the same. An author has to assume that the problems people can solve through reading are mild, and, furthermore, that his readers can ignore his advice or seek other opinions if he challenges them too severely, and so he feels it safe to lay all his cards on the table fast; a counselor has to make sure that he preserves his relationship with the patient at all costs and thus must feel his way by gradual give-and-take in many situations.

One of the tragedies of our overly inhibited society is the fact that almost no one gets to appreciate anyone else's wholesome or constructive sexual experience. Functions which are naturally *private* have become *super-secret*, to such an extent that each couple approaches this crucial phase of living without knowing what has worked well for other people, what difficulties lie ahead, and how problems can be avoided or met. If the couples in this book come alive for you as people, perhaps you can gain at least a shadow of such experience, and do so in a framework of frankness, compassion, and respect for the worth of sustained man-woman relationships. In the process, you may well gain helpful insights and resources for dealing with sexuality in yourself, your husband or wife, your children, and the world.

THE TROUBLED BED

1. Failure?

Some domestic squabbles actually help. But there is a point at which you need to call a halt. When attack and counterattack build until the man insults the woman's charm or the woman denies his manhood, anything further can do nothing but harm. The Armstrongs had reached that level frequently through the years, and hit it again in my office.

"You miserable clod!" Sarah Armstrong exclaimed, looking contemptuously at her husband. "You're just a front with nothing behind it."

Phil smiled. "Better than no front at all," he said, his eyes pointedly on her décolletage.

"You don't need a big bust to be a woman, but you need *something* to be a man."

It was up to me to keep this from going further.

"And you've put up with this for nine whole years," I exclaimed. "Lord, what a feeling you must have had for each other at the start."

Phil and Sarah stared at me, astonished. The idea seemed entirely new to them.

"And there must be *something* left of it," I went on, "or you would have given each other up years ago."

"Something left for *him?*" Sarah asked.

"You're both here," I said pointedly. "Let's go back a bit and see where things got off the track."

Sarah started by telling of one of Phil's insults. Phil countered with an account of her earlier offenses, and neither of them said anything constructive. I finally closed the session by saying:

"Look, we're trying to rebuild a marriage, not fix the blame for its failure. You two are in a vicious circle. One of you hurts the other, the other strikes back, and around and around you go. All that has nothing to do with the issue. If you're going to get together again, you'll have to figure out how you can meet each other's needs and make something out of your marriage, instead of deciding who was to blame for the trouble in the first place. We can't get any help from looking at the past if you're each trying to make the other a scapegoat. You have to look for con- structive points—not for ammunition in a continuing feud."

I wish I could report that the rehabilitation viewpoint took immediate hold on the Armstrongs. But it didn't. Our next three sessions were spent trying to turn this corner, with attack and counterattack, accusation and innuendo, all aimed at fixing blame.

Whenever I tried to broach the subject of sex, either

Phil or Sarah would lead the conversation off on another tack: sexual matters seldom come out freely at first. In our fourth session, we were talking about "plus points," and they gave each other quite a few.

"Sarah's a winner, except where I'm concerned," Phil said. "Top student, great at sports. She's been an officer of every organization she ever joined; she runs the house like a pro; she's the world's most conscientious mother."

"Phil's a top notcher in a lot of ways, too," Sarah said. "He gives his job everything he's got."

"So you're both used to succeeding," I said. "And you're both 'overachievers'—people who need success badly enough to go all out, hell bent, Devil take the hindmost, and then kick yourself around the block for every minor failure or miscue. In some ways, that's absolutely great, but in other ways it's not so pleasant. You're staking a lot on success when you let it become that important to you. Even the fear of failure can wake you up in a cold sweat, and the actual experience can be absolutely shattering."

Sarah veered away. "That's probably true," she said, "but I don't see how we can ever succeed if we don't get some of these other things straightened out. How can I feel anything for a person who treats me like he does? Like last night at dinner, for instance——."

"Before we go into that," I interrupted, "let's get back to sex. Sometimes you can tell what's wrong with a couple by what they *don't* talk about, and in your case sex heads the list. We've hardly had three sentences about it in three sessions."

They looked at each other and fidgeted a bit.

"Well, where do we start?" Phil asked. "It's just like the rest, not very good."

"Since when?" I asked. "Did you ever get satisfaction from each other? And do you get any satisfaction now?"

"It was all right on our honeymoon," Sarah said. "I

didn't expect very much, and Phil seemed satisfied. But the weeks went by, and still nothing happened. Once in a while I'd get stirred up and once in a great while I'd come. After a year, we still practically never came together, and I think we both knew it was a failure. From then on, it was just a matter of which one was to blame—me for being cold, or him for not knowing how."

"Or maybe both of you," I said, "for expecting too much."

"What do you mean?" Phil asked.

I shrugged and didn't answer. "Let's go back over the situation," I said. "You got along all right sexually at the start? That is, Phil was gentle with you, took time to get you ready, and didn't hurt you in the early days?"

"That's right."

"And you felt that you satisfied him completely at first? And felt fulfillment from satisfying him?"

"At first," she said. "Everything was fine those first few weeks. Then he changed somehow. He obviously expected something I wasn't giving him. He kept asking whether there wasn't something else he could do to make it right. He would stop right in the middle to ask whether I really wanted him and whether I was getting ready."

"But I wasn't worried about myself," Phil said. "Sure, I had expected we would both come together by then. But that wasn't why I worried. I just knew you weren't getting very much out of it, and I wanted things to be right for us both."

"This is just a few weeks after you were married," I said. "Did you both think Sarah should be reaching a climax by then?"

"Of course," Phil said. And Sarah nodded.

"What do you think about that now? Don't you think you might have been expecting too much?"

"Maybe a little," Phil said.

"Maybe a lot!" I said. "A woman's climax just isn't automatically part of intercourse, like a man's. Most women don't have a climax as much as half the time, and very few have one in their first few episodes."

"Then when *do* they?"

"Three months is average for first orgasm, but a lot of women who ultimately prove normally responsive don't have their first climax until they've been married nine months to a year or more. Then their average starts climbing. Most women report a steadily higher percentage of orgasms for at least five years after marriage.

"Even then, couples have to count themselves lucky if they both reach a climax fairly often. One third of women reach a climax only rarely—perhaps one orgasm in ten times. Another third ultimately get to the point where they reach a climax fairly frequently. So it is only about a third who have one most or all of the time."

"That's still a lot better than we've done," Sarah said.

"But you both became so concerned about your supposed failure at sexual intercourse that you couldn't possibly do well at it. Sexual excitement uses exactly the same nerve cells and fibers as other emotions such as anxiety and concern. You don't just 'relax and enjoy it'—you *have to* relax to enjoy it. But look at the way you were going at it: Phil questioning you at every stage, straining to reach an unattainable goal. You, wondering whether there's something wrong with you, examining every twinge of feeling that started to stir."

"I guess we were both trying too hard," Sarah said. "I know the few times I had a climax it actually sneaked up on me. We'd start making love while I was still half asleep and I'd be almost there before I realized it."

"That's the way it is with lots of couples. They don't

make it when they try for orgasm, and succeed when they relax. Particularly if they think there has to be something wrong if they have a 'failure.'

"If you think that you should be reaching orgasm every time you have intercourse, the prospect of failure alone involves enough anxiety to quench your ardor. When you assume that mutual orgasm is normal, your mind fills with doubts and concerns whenever you start with sex. 'Will I fail again this time?' you ask yourself. Or 'Don't we really love each other after all?' Or 'There has to be *something* wrong—with him or with me.'

"You just can't have this kind of idea, and the feelings that go with it, without muffling your sexual response. And the less you respond the more you doubt. So around and around it goes, getting worse instead of better."

"There must be more to it than that we can't succeed because we're too anxious," Phil said.

"By now, I'm sure there is. But let's take this one step at a time. A few weeks after you were married, you obviously felt concerned about your sex life."

"Concerned?" Sarah said. "He was so upset he practically shook. And I figured it was all my fault. I tried my best to respond, but it just didn't happen."

"I don't know," Phil said. "For a little while we seemed to get along all right."

Sarah laughed bitterly. "Maybe you thought it was all right. But that was only because I faked it. God, how I wanted to make you happy then. And nothing would do unless you thought I was with you. So I pretended when I didn't feel anything, and we got along fine for a while. I could really blow up your ego with a few gasps and snorts.

"But all of a sudden, it didn't seem right. One night I just couldn't stand it any more. We were right in the middle of sex and I started to cry, and he kept asking me why. I finally said that I never had liked it and the whole thing was a fraud. We've been at each other's throats off and on ever since."

The Armstrongs made a lot of progress in the next few minutes. They were both super-strivers who could not stand failure. The idea of sexual inadequacy had been too much for them. When it seemed that they were failing in this crucial sphere, each subconsciously blamed the other as a means of self-defense. And as in most marriage battles, each of them kept the real issue concealed even from himself and found excuses for venting his spleen on the other.

"All very fine," Phil said toward the end of the session. "Suppose we do still have some feeling left for each other after all these years. We still haven't made our sex life work, and you tell us that the harder we try the worse we'll do. That's an insoluble dilemma."

"It's not quite that bad," I said. "You just have to take it one step at a time and make sure each step is easy enough that you aren't under any pressure."

"How?"

"When you first started your sexual relations, you just tried to keep Sarah comfortable, without worrying about her having an orgasm. And she tried to satisfy *you* without worrying about herself. You were both trying to keep each other comfortable, to relieve each other's sexual tensions or fears, and to let sex happen often enough and naturally enough to let couple lovemaking build and develop. Now that's a pretty good framework for getting a fresh start in sex, too."

"Let's get a little more specific," Sarah said. "Just exactly what are we supposed to do?"

"First, you, Sarah, should forget all about orgasm for the moment. Don't wait for it, don't try for it, don't expect it. You've been making orgasm the measure of worth as a woman, and it isn't. Nobody can find the least fault with your sexual accomplishments if you keep your husband sexually satisfied, and as long as he doesn't fret about the situation your orgasms don't make a particle of difference in that respect.

"Second, make yourself available whenever Phil wants you, as long as you have comfortable surroundings and privacy. Phil can't stay sufficiently free of sexual tensions to do his best for either himself or you unless he has intercourse somewhere near as often as his nature demands. And incidentally, that probably won't be nearly as often as you might expect if you've been turning him down. Someone who bangs on the door forty times when it stays locked only knocks once if you open right away. Most wives who haven't reached sexual harmony with their husbands find them making some kind of advance every night. These women are afraid that they will be asked to participate more often than they can stand if they let down the barriers. But, actually, a man who gets all the sex he wants finds that in a week or two the pressure of his physical urge is relieved and the psychologic pressure to overcome resistance no longer applies, so his sex pace generally drops to something his wife finds acceptable."

Turning to Phil, I said: "Of course, you have obligations during this phase, too. First, you must be sure to cause no physical discomfort. You should use excessive lubrication—either petroleum jelly on the penis or K-Y in the vagina—though it may impair your pleasure slightly, instead of taking any chance of causing painful pinches or pulls upon your wife's delicate genital tissues. You'll need to introduce your penis gradually, giving the vagina plenty of chance to relax before you begin deep strokes. You'll find that your erection can be sustained very well by slight and gentle motions involving penetration only of the head, and so you won't fail sexually by going slowly.

"Second, you should work on improving your control. Your wife will cooperate much more freely if she sees that you are increasing your staying power so that she can be almost sure of adequate stimulation by the time she is passionately aroused.

"Third, you need to express your feelings as freely as possible during and after intercourse. It's awfully easy for your wife to feel abused at this point. She gets no physical pleasure from unimpassioned intercourse and has to take her satisfaction from an awareness of what she is doing for you and for the marriage. The more freely you communicate (partly by words, but mainly by caresses, gestures, and facial expressions) the more fulfillment she enjoys.

"Finally, you have to be considerate. If your wife is going to accept you willingly whenever you make advances, you can't impose this duty at vastly inconvenient times— just when she's dressing for a party, or when it's time to start cooking a meal, for instance."

Phil and Sarah agreed somewhat reluctantly to this program, but once they agreed, they followed it completely. And the results were somewhat surprising. After only three weeks, Phil asked me: "Is it OK for us to move into the next phase? The other night Sarah felt an urge, but things have worked out so well so far that we didn't want to spoil the situation by rushing it."

I explained that there was no reason to hang back, so long as neither of them turned *hopes* and *inclinations* into *expectations* or *demands*. In a few weeks they reported a new high in sexual harmony. And while "they lived happily ever after" would be too strong a statement, they have since built a sound and lasting marriage.

As we have seen, totally unrealistic expectations got the Armstrongs off to a bad start in the sexual field. They both believed that a couple who love each other should ultimately reach orgasm simultaneously almost every time, and that they should reach this point during or soon after their honeymoon. When they fell short of this almost unreachable goal, each began to doubt his own sexual capability. Self-doubt in this vital sphere then caused intolerable anxiety and a vicious circle of blame-casting and defensive counterattack.

When your marriage fails to live up to your expectations in the sexual sphere, you generally blame yourself, your partner, or the quality of your love. You react to the pressure of these doubts and inadequacies in distinctly harmful ways. You almost never go back to fundamentals and ask, "Was this really a shortcoming, or did we simply expect too much?"

Perhaps the basic vice is in keeping score. We Americans are born (or quickly bred) competitors. Whether we count our success in dollars, in lives saved, or in souls converted, we never fail to rate ourselves in some way. But score-keeping in terms of feminine orgasm does nothing but harm. Happy couples have no reason to keep score, and have good reasons not to. When you think in mathematical terms, you fix your attention on deficiencies and introduce a "salesman's quota" type of pressure that can quench desire, dampen ardor, and thoroughly disrupt emotional communion.

Sexual scorekeeping, I emphasize, does nothing but harm, and yet almost everyone who feels any doubt about sexual success as an individual or as a couple automatically engages in it. Comparison with the "normal" is inevitable, too, but you can avoid substantial discomfiture by replacing romantically inflated myths with real facts.

For example, a great many people have gotten the idea (either from books or from each other) that orgasm gives far more pleasure to both partners if they enjoy it simultaneously than if they miss by even a few seconds. Actually, each partner's orgasm stimulates the other's genitals in special ways. The vagina contracts in waves of motion to stimulate the male. The jet spray of the male emission stimulates the female. These effects when added to those of continuing sexual activity often spur the lagging partner into orgasm. This type of succession—one partner's climax causing stimulations which bring the other to orgasm a few moments later—occurs much more commonly than a split-second simultaneous orgasm.

If simultaneous orgasm provided a unique sexual experience, perhaps it would still be worth striving for. However, only very unsophisticated couples generally find mutual orgasm causing much difference. The instinctive movements which a woman makes when approaching and enjoying orgasm give both her partner and herself greater pleasure than they would have if she were inactive, but such instinctive movements do not increase stimulation any more than—and often not as much as—movements made by deliberate lovemaking technique. Male instinctive movement, on the other hand, is much less likely to produce in a woman prolonged ecstatic transportation (just short of orgasm) or slow peaked orgasms than is a deliberate wife-pleasing maneuver. Most highly responsive wives get their greatest satisfaction from one of the earlier climaxes in a multiple orgasm episode rather than from the final flurry, and sexually competent couples rarely see any benefit whatever in split-second simultaneousness.

The echoing and reechoing of mutual pleasure, as each partner enjoys his loved one's emotional response as well as his own, certainly makes mutually gratifying incidents much more fulfilling than occasions when one partner complies mainly for the other's sake. But this emotional spiral envelops the whole occasion rather than operating moment by moment, and perfect timing makes little or no difference to it.

The gains from simultaneous orgasm definitely do not offset the quenched desires which result from striving toward it. You should unquestionably forget all about simultaneous orgasm as a sexual objective, and certainly should not count yourself a failure if you never experience it.

If you ask young men how often they expect a loving wife to have orgasm, they may tell you: "Every time, once she's had a chance to develop her feminine nature."

How long will that take? A few days to a few weeks, never longer, in their opinion.

Young women generally have somewhat more realistic but nevertheless exaggerated expectations in this area.

The tragedy of these excessive expectations is that virtually everyone falls short of them. Doubts about the husband's sexual capability, the wife's responsiveness and/or the quality of their love then poison the union with anxiety and insecurity. Husbands often consider themselves sexual failures when their wives fail to reach orgasm, even if the wife is perfectly content. The resulting anxieties, loss of confidence, and guilt cause both personal discomfiture and sexual impediment. Realistic or scaled-down expectations in this sphere therefore help husbands as well as wives.

Wifely orgasm develops much more slowly and much less consistently than most people believe. As I mentioned to the Armstrongs, about one third of women have orgasm either rarely or not at all. Another third receive passionate reward only about half the time. About one third of the long-married, contented wives report orgasm during

almost every sexual incident, but even these generally find
that the rewards of various episodes vary from the occasional failure through frequent ordinary but pleasant
sessions to infrequent explosions.

Sexual scorekeeping in terms of feminine orgasm im-
plies that a passionate climax offers the woman's only
reward. Most of my sexually successful patients would
dispute this notion. As one very sincere and knowledgeable
lady put it: "Sure, I enjoy having orgasm. But that's just
the frosting on the cake. When I can please my husband—
when I know he loves me and needs me and is entirely
satisfied with me—that's enough to make the whole thing
worthwhile."

Certainly, a woman can and *should* feel sexually adequate if she can satisfy her husband whether she has
orgasm frequently, occasionally, or very rarely indeed.
Neither what she *gets* from sex nor what she *gives* her
mate through it depends on the frequency of her orgasms.
More orgasms and more intense orgasms are valid aims of
improved sexual technique, but the batting average does
not have to reach any predetermined level before both
husband and wife feel fully adequate and sexually proved.

Most people equate male sexual capability with potency,
which they judge in terms of how often, not how well.
Two of my cases suffered from this problem in completely
different ways.

George S. was Mabel's second husband and suffered constantly from comparisons with her first.

"He should have teamed up with a librarian or something, not with me," Mabel said. "Two, maybe three times
a month and he's through! What kind of sex life is that?"

George's sex drive was well within the normal range

(which is broad enough to include quite a variation). Mabel's true sex pace wasn't very far from what he was giving, either. But she felt that *something* was missing, that they weren't getting along quite as well as they should, and so she fixed upon his slightly slower sex pace as one cause for which she need not share the blame. Actually, her carping generated anxieties which kept George from indulging as often as he otherwise might. The fact that she had made an issue of his "inadequacy" created one more problem in a marriage already plagued by numerous doubts and uncertainties. When I persuaded her to make herself available, but not to make demands or belittle George's urge, his pace almost doubled within a few short weeks, and at least one problem vanished from their strife-ridden life.

At the other extreme, Mildred B. had only one complaint about her husband: "He wants sex all the time—every single night. The only rest I get is during my period, and sometimes not even then."

"All I'm trying to do is be normal," her husband said. "Everybody says 'three or four times a week anyway' for a young healthy guy."

Since his sex pace wasn't actually that fast, he was more than willing to slow down once he realized that he could do so without seeming abnormal. When he wasn't forcing himself in order to prove he was normal, his natural inclinations proved quite harmonious with those of his wife.

What is a normal pace, anyway? There simply is no satisfactory answer. Couples who get along perfectly well in the sexual sphere may have intercourse anywhere from a few times a year to several times a night (the record setter, according to the Kinsey report, was a professor who had intercourse about twenty times each week). Numbers reflect couple adjustment and current emotional state as much as they reflect masculine capability. Almost every husband experiences surges in potency when he takes a vacation and letdowns when business pressure or family dissension bother him. Sex remains a couple affair, with the general state of the emotional relationship, the wife's attitudes, sexual competence, and many other factors entering into the matter of how often a husband can have a firm erection.

So instead of judging masculine capacity by sex pace, why not measure male performance by its effectiveness? Does the husband's pace match or exceed the wife's? Then there can be no question of adequacy, and further "potency" may harm couple harmony. Does the wife need more sexual stimulation than the husband naturally provides? Then he has to depend on skill and caress instead of instinct, but that does not really make him less of a man or doom the couple to an inferior sex life in any way.

We have seen, then, that exaggerated sexual expectations play a part in many (if not most) less-than-perfect marriages. The anxieties and feelings of inferiority they engender cause everything from minor interference with relaxed enjoyment of sex to total disruption. Very few of the couples involved figure out the source of their problem until the vicious circles of self-doubt or accusation have led them into substantial difficulty. But if the pressure is taken off and the sex life gradually rebuilt, problems which stem from this source usually prove easy to solve.

2. Preparation for Intercourse

"We've got just one problem," Joe Madigan said. "I come too fast when we have intercourse. Mary practically never has her climax while we're together."

"We can get along this way if we have to," Mary Madigan added. "But when I mentioned it to my doctor he suggested that you might be able to give us some help."

When people state their sex problems in plain and unembarrassed fashion, their prospects almost always prove to be pretty good. Couples who have deep-seated emotional turmoils can seldom talk openly about sex on the first visit, much less in their first utterance. So I felt hopeful about the Madigans right from the start.

"How long have you been married?" I asked.

"Seven years," Mary said. "And we get along fine in every other way. It's just this sex thing that bothers us."

"Then you've never had a climax during intercourse?"

"It's not that bad. I come occasionally before he's finished, but not very often, and it seems to be happening less and less."

I turned to Joe.

"You say you finish too fast," I said. "Exactly how fast? Do you ever have an orgasm before you make contact?"

"You mean before my penis is inside? No. But sometimes I only make a few movements and I'm done— nowhere near long enough to give Mary a chance."

"And that's always the way?"

"Sometimes a little better than others, but never more than a minute at most."

"And it's been the same all along, ever since you were married?"

"Just about. I can't see any improvement, anyway, and we've been married seven years."

My first job with the Madigans was to exclude physical disease. Joe's story of constant difficulty for several years almost ruled out prostate infection, but I questioned him carefully about low backache, burning urination, difficulty starting the urinary stream, and other urinary problems. He had no such evidence of prostate trouble, and his gland passed the usual tests.

The other disorder which sometimes causes premature ejaculation is a bit harder to rule out. Some men get a cyst of the verumontanum—a pocket of fluid just at the junction of the sexual and the urinary passages—which causes a sexual climax to occur almost immediately after erection. Most men who suffer from this condition reach a climax before they can even make sexual entrance, at

least on some occasions. And their climax is not particularly satisfying; though they have discharged semen and
lost erection, they still feel sexually excited rather than
content. To detect such a cyst, a urologist puts an optical
instrument up the penis; if a cyst exists, it can be burned
out painlessly with an electrical spark and in a week or
ten days the patient is cured. Joe proved not to have this
condition either, and so the problem seemed to be with
sex techniques.

We went over the couple's approach to intercourse very
thoroughly.

"Let's assume that you're both in the mood," I said.
"What do you do?"

Joe and Mary looked at each other.

"Well, we start off with a few kisses," Mary said.

"Then I usually pet a bit," Joe went on. "In fact, I use a
finger to get her as close as I can. I'm so darn fast after we
get started that I try to get her right to the brink first."

"And does she do anything special at that point?"

"Just lets me do what I want."

"Actually," Mary said, "I've leaned over backward not
to stimulate him. Joe even avoids some things he likes to
do to me, like kissing my breasts and playing with my
nipples, because they excite him so. And I keep strictly
hands off—I'm even a little careful about how I kiss him."

"All so that he won't get ahead of you?" I asked. Both
of them nodded miserably.

I paused and looked from one to the other. "This is the
kind of situation which happens quite often, and neither
of you is really to blame. You have tried to use common
sense instead of information to solve your sex problems,
and common sense has led you astray."

"What do you mean?" Joe asked.

"It seems like common sense to stimulate a man less

before he makes his entrance if he has a climax too soon after he's in, but actually this practice does more harm than good. The problem is that *rapid change in stimulation* rather than *amount of stimulation* trips the male trigger. If a man ejaculates too quickly, his problem is usually that the *change in stimulation* at the moment of entrance is too much for him. If he gets *less* stimulation beforehand, there is *more* change at the moment of entrance and he has still greater difficulty."

"So what's the right thing to do?" Mary asked.

"Just the opposite of what you would think—stimulate him *more* before intercourse. Not only longer but more intensely. You should not only let him do what he wants with you, but also caress his body, including his genitals, over a considerable period of time."

"I still don't quite see how that works," Mary said.

"If you stimulate him more and more intensely beforehand, his sexual entrance will involve less change. Gradually increasing stimulation over a period of several minutes will not trigger a climax, as long as you avoid a few specific caresses. And you will gain in several other ways by more intense stimulation before intercourse."

"Such as?" Joe asked.

"There's your wife's condition. If *she* stimulates *you* more and longer before you make sexual entrance, *you* will wind up stimulating *her* more and longer, too. You'll caress Mary all the while she is caressing you, and her organs will respond by relaxing thoroughly and producing lubricating secretions. So when you enter, it will be in a looser, slicker vagina, one without the same friction and pressure which sets you off now."

"But what if she goes ahead and has an orgasm?"

"That won't hurt a thing! Most women can get ready for a second or third climax much more quickly than they reach the first, so if you play past a climax Mary will probably be able to respond more quickly and more completely than usual. Just keep on caressing each other until her excitement is on the rise again.

"But there is one point here that deserves emphasis. I said *caressing each other*. If an early orgasm causes any problems at all in couple sex harmony, it's because the woman gets so enraptured that she forgets to continue to caress her husband. Mary can enjoy an early climax thoroughly, but she shouldn't yield herself to it so completely that she forgets to caress you actively all the while."

There was a brief lull in our discussion while the Madigans thought the matter over.

"Could you tell us exactly what we are supposed to do?"

"I'll show you," I said. "If neither of you objects, we'll go into the examining room to see what we are talking about."

One of my sociologist friends did a study of nudist camps and had to leave his clothes behind on every visit. He told me afterwards:

"It's amazing how quickly you break through inhibitions about exposing yourself. You worry all the way there about how you're going to stand it, and five minutes after you're inside the only thing you miss about your clothes is the pockets."

Knowing the way most people can overcome their nudity taboos in a doctor's office, I started some time ago to talk from life instead of using plastic models to demonstrate where to do what. This procedure has proved very helpful in several ways. Translating advice on sex technique from book or lecture to real life always causes some uncertainty and sometimes causes downright error, while if someone actually points out such organs as the clitoris, both husband and wife know exactly where they are. Showing couples that they can expose themselves to each other and approach sex problems openly—that they can look at or touch each other's bodies without interfering with the emotional appeal they have for each other in a different setting—also has proved helpful. Several couples have reported that this factor aided later communications and helped them to straighten out problems.

Sexual excitement has never once become a factor in these conferences. No male has had an erection either while looking at or handling his wife's organs or while being handled to the extent necessary to show the different portions of the genitals, and no female has showed signs or reported sensations of sexual fervor. Part of this detachment comes from the clinical setting: When a person is put on an examining table and draped as if for medical examination, the circumstances are not associated with lovemaking or romance. But most of the detachment seems to stem from mental attitude. I strongly suspect that if *you* and *your mate* are reasonably uninhibited, you might make real gains by alternately draping each other for examination, looking at each other's sex organs in a good light and in circumstances more clinical than romantic, and discussing briefly what areas need gentle touch, which spots can stand firm friction, and so forth. You might or might not learn anything, but you'll almost certainly gain confidence, and squelch any residues of false modesty in your marriage.

I started with Mary stripped, draped, and on the table.

"A woman gets much more from general body caress than a man does," I began. "Maybe half of her buildup of sexual excitement comes from kisses, breast play, and nongenital caresses. A man gets only about one-tenth of his stimulation from such sources—never enough to cause a climax—with the rest concentrated in the genitals.

"Kisses and caresses help you not only to *build* but also to *judge* the state of Mary's sexual excitement. When you kiss her, you get a pretty good idea of whether she's interested in sex. When you caress her nipple, you can get a pretty good idea of whether her excitement is building. As you know, the nipple becomes larger and much firmer when she begins to get excited. These tiny bumps on the brown halo around the nipple also stand out much more sharply during sexual excitement. The nipple becomes soft again (but perhaps a bit more elastic than usual) when your wife approaches a climax.

"These breast changes correspond closely to those occurring in the clitoris. When the nipples are fully erect, the clitoris is usually firm and responds keenly to caress. When the nipple becomes soft again, the clitoris has usually 'retracted' and other forms of genital caress work better. So breast play not only helps you to excite your wife and judge her readiness but also guides your choice of genital caress.

"At the beginning, when the nipple is still soft, gentle caresses work best. You can run your finger, the palm of your hand, your lips, or your tongue across or around the nipple and the surrounding area. When it becomes firm, you can stimulate more vigorously. Roll it between your fingers, flip it gently with your fingertip, pinch it between lip-covered teeth, twang it with the tip of your tongue. You might well find that Mary will have an orgasm occasionally from breast play alone—lots of women do."

"What about other body areas?" Joe asked. "I've read magazine articles about erogenous spots where caresses prove extra exciting."

"Like the earlobes, buttocks, inside surface of thighs,

and so forth? Most girls have some such spots, but they aren't really that specific or that important. Gentle stroking soothes and excites most women whether you work upward from their fingertips or knees and whether you touch the earlobes or the neck. But you can pretty well explore that territory for yourself—as long as you keep to gentle caresses you can't do any harm, and this fits into love play early enough that a false start won't break the buildup.

"Let's get down to the genital area. Most people don't experiment too much here, either because they're afraid of causing pain or because they think they might stumble into perversion. When you figure that most couples make love in the dark and that the distance between tender and tough or between proper and perverse is rather small, these fears make a certain amount of sense. But you ought to be able to get rid of them by knowing what you are doing. Let me wash up a moment, and we'll take a look."

Since so many people have the idea that sex organs are dirty, I've always made it a point to use bare hands in demonstrating sexual anatomy. And I deliberately wash *before* instead of *after* such contact, explaining that even clean hands have hundreds of times as many germs as the vagina.

When we had positioned ourselves so that Joe could see well, I spread the outer lips of Mary's organ slightly.

"When Mary gets excited sexually," I said, "things will be a little different. The inner lips here will increase in size, often to double their present thickness. In the process, they will push the outer lips aside, more or less as I'm doing with my fingers, and expose both the inner surfaces and a bit of the underlying vagina. That's why you can usually make sexual entrance easily even though the exact spot seems a bit concealed now. But the surface layer remains just as thin as you see it here—about fifty times thinner than the skin on your back. And this area has few glands to lubricate it. Almost all the lubricating moisture has to spread down from inside the vagina. The tissues here are very sensitive, so that even gentle stroking will seem a bit harsh if they are dry."

"I've had a pinching sensation once in a while when Joe's caressing me," Mary said. "And sometimes when he starts intercourse. Is that what you mean?"

"Probably. These tissues are among the most sexually sensitive in a woman's body, but many husbands shy away from them just because caressing them dry causes pain. But Joe can lubricate the tissues by using his finger to transfer a little of the fluid from inside the vagina to them. Or you can use an artificial lubricant like K-Y Jelly. Then, Joe, you will be able to try stroking the surface with a finger, catching the lips between the middle sections of two bent fingers, catching them between the tip of your thumb and your index finger, and rubbing or stroking them. Light, gentle touch on the inside or the outside surface of these folds provides an exquisite sensation. Incidentally, caresses of the inner lips can stir excitement all the way to orgasm, while the clitoris, which gets so much publicity as the touchbutton of feminine passion, pulls back and becomes less sensitive just before the climax."

"Where exactly is Mary's clitoris?" Joe asked.

"You see where the inner lips meet at the front of the vagina? The clitoris is about half an inch in front of that junction. It doesn't stick out above the surface, so you can't see where it is. You can feel it slightly now, but it becomes larger and firmer with sexual excitement. Mary's clitoris feels about as big as the clip on your automatic pencil, but the size varies.

"As you can see, the clitoris is buried beneath some loose tissue. The silky, gentle caresses which work best on the inner lips don't penetrate to the clitoris. You have to press a bit more firmly either over the tip, the shaft, or the base of the clitoris and roll your fingertip or move it a short distance in either direction, so that the tender surface layer can roll under or move with your finger instead of being pulled or pinched.

"You can stimulate the clitoris best when it is erect, which usually corresponds to the time when the nipples are very firm. When Mary gets near a climax, you can still give her pleasure by stimulating the clitoris area, but in-and-out movements of the finger or the penis along the front rim of the vagina work better than clitoral massage near orgasm; probably these caresses work largely by creating drag on the clitoral area, since the clitoris itself is hard to find or stimulate toward the end. And, remember, gentle frictions along the inner lips continue to be exciting all the way through."

"Wait a minute," Joe said. "Won't it do more harm than good if I try to think of all this while we're making love?"

"That's why I'm trying to help you learn it now. This is like a demonstration of a dance step—learn the technique now or in a second look later and it will come naturally when the occasion arises.

"Now let's take a look at the vagina itself. When you spread the inner lips slightly, you can see the dividing line between smooth, thin tissue at the outside and ridged or deeply wrinkled tissue farther in. The ridged or deeply wrinkled tissue is vagina, and it's a lot tougher than the surface structures. Its also much less sensitive. It hasn't any of the nerve endings which normally signal light touch or tickling sensations. Moreover, this tissue has countless lubricating glands of its own, so that it is always moist and well lubricated once the woman is aroused. About the only way you can hurt this tissue is to overstretch it, and that's almost impossible to do with a finger. So your caresses here can be firm and vigorous without fear of causing discomfort.

"Perhaps this is a good time to mention the matter of size. You don't have to fill the vagina to stimulate it. Women who masturbate generally find a slender object like a pencil more stimulating than one which matches the penis in size and contour. So a one-finger caress is usually as good as a two-finger and better than three, which can cause a painful stretch somewhere even in the most relaxed vagina."

"Do you just move your finger in and out?" Joe asked.

"Or twirl your fingertip in circles, rub it from side to side, put in two fingers and make crawling motions, rub your index finger in and out along the front of the vagina while titillating the clitoris or inner lips with your thumb —there are a dozen combinations you can work out.

"There is one other highly sensitive structure you should know about. That's the urethra, the tube from the bladder to the outside. When I spread the inner lips, you can see its outer opening right here—halfway in between the meeting of the inner lips at the front and the opening of the vagina at the back. From there the tube runs in front of the vagina and in back of the pubic bone, right in the middle. As you can see, it's buried in fairly firm tissue, so you can't stimulate it with light touch. When Mary has become thoroughly aroused, though, stimulation of the urethra will give her a tremendous thrill. The only way to get at the urethra is by rubbing firmly enough with the fingertip to penetrate all the intervening tissue, and you have to be sure that the vagina is thoroughly moist before you press that hard. Be sure to keep your fingernails trimmed, or use the pulp of your finger instead of its tip. Only caresses in the midline do any good—there are no sensitive structures off to the side. You need to be careful not to carry your caresses outside the tough vagina itself—if you run over into the thin, sensitive vestibule you might cause discomfort. But all you have to do is learn where to do what now, while it's all in front of your eyes, and you won't have a bit of trouble."

After a few minutes' further discussion, it was Joe's turn to get on the table. Only his genitals were bared; a sheet covered the rest of his body.

"Mary, you can build some male excitement by kissing each other, and he will get some thrill out of running his hands over your body or caressing you. But the vast bulk of his ardor comes from right here in the genital area. Even here, most areas are not sensitive enough to bring him to a climax. Take the scrotum, for instance. This thin bag of skin holds the testicles. It is very sensitive to touch, and when a man feels in the mood any caress here excites him. I've always compared caresses of the scrotum in the husband with caresses of the breast in the wife. They fit in about the same time period, when you're already excited and sexually attuned but not yet ready for intercourse. Gentle touch plays the biggest role in both, though firmer pinches and rolling the tissue between the fingers to stimulate underlying structures also works. But I've never known a man to reach a climax from stimulation of the scrotum, though many women have from breast caresses, and so the scrotum would seem a little less sensitive than the breast."

"You mean that I can tickle or pinch or pet this area without any risk of pushing Joe into a climax?"

"That's right. Or put your fingers underneath and

bobble the testes. Any kind of caress you can think of won't hurt a thing here, as long as it's fairly gentle—the testicles themselves are rather tender, and pinching or crushing *them* definitely hurts.

"The top and sides of the penis's shaft falls into a similar category. Until you get almost to the organ's head, caresses from gentle touch to painful pinch (effective toward the last moment, when pain nerves become sexually attuned) excite your husband without driving him toward a climax. Stroking, drumming with the fingers, petting, or pinching all stimulate and excite without causing ejaculation.

"This is the most important single thing you can do to help your sex life. As long as you continue this kind of caress, your husband will neither lose his erection nor ejaculate prematurely. So he can prolong the play phase as long as either of you wants or needs to."

"So anything goes along the top or sides of the penis, out almost to its head?"

"Not quite. The areas along the bottom of the penis and at the margin of its head are very sensitive. If you grasp the sides of the penis firmly enough to pull the skin on these sensitive spots or caress the penis in such a way that the whole skin moves up and down along the shaft, you could overexcite your husband. But even these caresses won't hurt if you limit them to a few brief movements at a time, and you don't have to be afraid of doing anything you happen to think of as long as you keep changing the position and type of your caress."

"But what about the tip of the penis? Is that so much more sensitive than the shaft?"

"Not at all. The head of the penis has the same kind of blunted sensitivity as the vagina—pain and temperature nerves only, without any touch or pressure fibers. Light stroking or petting here is simply futile. I've had a lot of patients who found that fact quite interesting, incidentally, because they had worried about whether there was something wrong with them until I mentioned it. A man simply cannot feel light touch or tickling on the head of his penis, whether he's aroused or not.

"His urinary tube is another matter. Like the woman's, a man's urethra has nerves which spur him keenly toward a climax once he feels sexually excited. This tube gets close to the body surface near the back of the scrotum and runs along the bottom surface of the penis to its tip. You can press one or more fingertips or your thumb up between the testes and rub back and forth along the urethra. It takes firm pressure, and you have to be sure that your fingernails don't dig in or pinch, but this caress adds variety without hastening a climax. Any pressing or rubbing along the urethra between the base and the tip of the penis can cause a climax if it is sustained for more than a few seconds. Such caresses can add spice and variety if used momentarily between other varieties, but they should not be long sustained."

"Is this what you're talking about?" Mary asked, pointing toward the area. "It seems quite a bit broader than the opening at the tip."

"Yes, the urethra itself is surrounded by a layer of muscle so that the outer dimension of the structure you feel is several times as large as the urinary passage. When Joe has an erection, everything under the skin will become hard except the urethra and its companion structures, so you'll be able to identify it down to the base of the shaft. At the top of the scrotal cavity the urethra has extra muscles around it. These become firm when Joe tries to cut off the flow of urine, so he can make them stand out for you very easily if you need to identify them.

"Now let's get to the most sensitive area in the male—

the skin just short of the penis's head. On the bottom side, where the urethra runs from the head to the shaft, there's this little cord of tissue called the frenulum. Once Joe gets aroused, any touch, pull, stretch or pinch on the frenulum will excite him greatly. This area is sensitive enough that repeated or prolonged caresses here will cause a climax, but brief caresses will provide great pleasure. Stroking, patting, flipping, or tapping this spot adds a wonderful variation on milder forms of genital fondling. Again, though, any caress which stimulates this area strongly, like pinching or tugging or stretching it by grasping the skin of the shaft, may push excitement to the point where Joe is ready for intercourse almost immediately. These caresses are the best way to get him to go ahead when you are as ready as you can ever get and don't want to actually *tell* him what to do."

"Pinching and tugging sound pretty rough for a sensitive spot," Mary said.

"Joe won't mind. Actually, the frenulum is sensitive sexually but pretty tough and hard to hurt. You can even pinch it between your finger and thumb, then roll it back and forth while continuing to pinch. Actually, Mary, with the particular kind of trouble you two have been having, you probably should make it a point to stimulate the frenulum only very briefly. But don't neglect it altogether. This is one spot that lets you turn a minor urge into keen excitement for Joe, and you'll find it playing a bigger and bigger part in your sex life as you learn couple control.

"Some sex experts think that the frenulum and the skin just behind the penis's head play a big part in bringing on orgasm, not through direct stimulation but through the tugging on this area during intercourse. Whether this is true or not, I do know that you can excite and stimulate your husband by tugging the loose skin of the penis shaft back toward his body—but again, not for more than a few moments at a time, or you will risk a climax."

"Tugging how?" Mary asked.

"You can pinch up enough of the loose skin of the shaft to get a grip, press a thumb and finger against the sides of the shaft, or grab the whole shaft in your fist. Caresses which massage the urethra while causing pull at the crown push toward climax more than the others, so you should probably avoid grasping the organ for very long. I think it's important to realize, though, that *nothing* you do for a moment or two will cause orgasm. Just keep changing one caress to another.

"For another fillip just before sexual entrance, you can try the 'snake bite' technique. Grasp the shaft with one hand and the penis head with the other, with your hands quite near each other; then twist one hand one way and the other in the opposite direction. The skin between them will be stretched in a shearing type of torsion which will give a very exciting sexual jolt."

Most marriage counselors claim that couples with sexual difficulties can generally work out the *physical* side of their relationship if they get the *emotional* side straight. There's something to be said for this position. A woman with substantial hang-ups in the sexual sphere simply cannot caress her husband actively enough to solve a problem like the Madigans'. Even if her inhibitions are only average size she needs to love him and want greatly to bring him pleasure before she will be willing to try genital fondling or caress.

Nevertheless, I've seen a lot of "Madigans," people who just don't know what to do. And one instructive session has often turned their sex life from a dissension-breeding trial to a harmony-inducing joy.

There is no panacea for sexual difficulties in marriage, but prolonged, intense genital play before sexual entrance comes surprisingly close to being one. This remedy almost always helps overcome fast male climax. It often helps with "frigidity" from inadequate preliminary play (the result of the husband's fear of losing erection). And it often helps with "impotency" by firming up and sustaining erection for a jaded or inhibited male.

The actual couples whose problem the Madigans represent have scored higher than any other group I've seen in one-visit cures. Over 80 percent have reported benefit when we made follow-up contacts later, all on the basis of improved sex technique without prolonged counseling. In fact, there's so little give-and-take involved in advising on this particular situation that readers might well find the tools for a self-help program right in this chapter.

3. Sex versus Love

"I'll bet I know what you thought," I told John Layton.
"You thought she had been faking it—playing you along
until you married her."

"Wouldn't anyone?" John answered. "From oohs and
ahs to tears and screeches—that's what happened to our
sex life after we walked down the aisle. Wouldn't you
think you'd been sold a bill of goods? She talks now about
expectations I never met—says that my lovemaking never
does anything for her. Well, I had expectations too. I
expected things to keep on like they'd been. And what
happened? She gives it to me whenever I want it, says
everything is great, then we get married and—"

"Oh, stop it!" his wife Kathy broke in. "You always talk about being entitled to sex, as if I could cook up passion for you like a dish of beef stew. Well, I can't turn a dial and get passionate. I can't 'give it to you' whenever you want—I can't even do it whenever *I* want, not the way I'm tied up in knots about it."

"In other words, you feel as if he just wants to use you instead of making love to you," I said.

"That's right. To him, sex is sex, period—it doesn't mean a thing otherwise. He even acts mad at me when he's starting—as if I'd just better not dare to hold out on him."

"So I'm mad," John said. "Why not? All I want is what I'm entitled to. And I'm not rough with her or anything."

"You want to have sex," I said. "She wants to make love. To women they're two very different things, but lots of men think they're almost the same."

"There's a difference, all right," John said. "You can have sex sometimes when you don't give a damn about what happens to the other person, but if you're going to be living together, you've got to make it as good as you can. I mean otherwise you'll spoil it for yourself in the long run."

"So it's a matter of giving strictly to get?"

"No. There's more to it than that. Everybody knows that the best kind of sex is when the woman responds. God knows I've tried to get Kathy going over and over. I *want* her to respond, that's for sure. I do everything I can to make it right for her."

"Everything?" Kathy asked. "Maybe, in terms of the mechanics. He's never really rough or anything, I've got to admit. But I get the feeling that I'm almost incidental. He's having his fun, and he's not even thinking of me except as a bedmate. Besides, he doesn't even seem to care whether I'm in the mood or not. I just don't have anything to say about when we do it. It makes me feel so low—like I'm some kind of a nothing he can order around."

"Now that's not 'having sex' versus 'making love,' " I said. "That's 'who's boss' and 'how does each of you rate?' "

"What do you mean?"

"You're talking now about whether John can be master without your being slave, and whether he has any right to be master in the first place."

"You mean love, honor, and obey? Taken literally?"

"No, but something happens to the control of your sex life as a couple after you walk down the aisle. And new husbands and wives almost always disagree over exactly what the change should be. Take yourselves, for instance. I'll bet that as long as you were single John never went ahead without your consent—that *you* really decided how often, when, where, and even how intercourse was to happen."

"That's right," Kathy said. "He made some kind of pass almost every night, of course, but he didn't get repulsive about it—if I said no it was no. Once we were married though, it was as if he owned me, and he didn't even ask."

"Well, maybe I haven't handled the preliminaries right," John said. "But I have some rights, don't I?"

"I suppose you do," she replied reluctantly. "But that isn't what you *really* want, is it—that I let you go ahead when there's nothing, no feeling at all?"

"But how do we ever get where things are right? If the only way I can get it is to fight you for it?"

"You can't," I said. "But I think if you both understand what's been going on you'll find that there's plenty of middle ground. The first point is that the control of couple sex *does* change with marriage, and that this change *does* create problems. It's not a matter of rights, though, with the male suddenly boss over the female as 'head of

the household' or something. It's a matter of sexual physiology and *couple* welfare."

"What do you mean?" Kathy asked.

"If either of you is going to get the most out of your sex
life, John has to be able to perform well. He has to stay
within the range of his own sex pace: push him too hard
and he won't have an erection; starve him out and he may
either lose potency through congestion or ejaculate before
you get a chance. So he has to have at least enough control
of the sex pace to stay within *his* range if *you're* ever going
to get full satisfaction. And he needs some control during
each episode, too. You both have to help keep his excitement at a level which maintains erection without causing
too quick a climax, and that's a lot easier if he pretty well
sets the pace."

"So you're telling me to take orders."

"Not exactly. I'm saying that if *you're* going to get full
satisfaction from sex both the number of episodes and the
level of activity within an episode have to suit John pretty
well. Now how do *you* think that can be arranged?"

"Well, I don't know. But why was it any different before
we got married? Why didn't we have this trouble when
we were just engaged?"

"Because after the wedding John expected to be master
of the bed if not the house, while you expected to keep the
same kind of control as to when, where, and how that you
had during courtship. Then, too, John didn't expect much
change in the amount of satisfaction he had to give you,
while you almost certainly believed that marriage would
bring increasing physical pleasure from sex, that you were
entitled to such pleasure, and were being cheated if you
didn't get it. Things *couldn't* work out to meet these
contradictory expectations for both of you. But each of
you still found the failure shocking; you reacted to it, and
you've been reacting ever since. You've been hurt and

mad, and as a result have said things to each other that have made matters that much worse. But there's no reason you can't get together, if you get down to the basic issues. So let's get back to this one: For your sake as well as for his own, John needs considerable say-so in your sex life. How do you think he ought to go about getting it?"

"Why can't he *ask* me? Or do a little courting like he did before? He didn't club me over the head then."

"So all right," John said. "You give in whenever I'm halfway welcome, and I'll try my best to make it right. Let's not go on with this now. I think we've both got the idea, and we'll have to try it before we'll know if we need more help. One thing I want to say: I *do* love you. Maybe I've been too busy throwing my weight around to show it, but I want this thing to work. If you do too . . ."

It wasn't that easy, of course. John and Kathy worked for several months to build a good marriage. But they turned an important corner that first day when they realized that a long-term deep relationship is built of different stuff from a short-term, superficial one. Marriage is as different from courtship as running a resort is from taking a vacation there. Moreover, men have radically different ideas from women as to how several basic problems in long-range relations should be handled.

Having sex versus *making love* is one such issue. A great many men treat sex as a commodity or service rather than as a means of expressing affection for a mate. Most couples will benefit considerably if they adopt the "female" viewpoint and treat intercourse as a meaningful caress instead of either an obligation or a tit-for-tat service. The "female" viewpoint makes every caress and sexual movement into an act of love. This gives sex a great deal of extra meaning for both husband and wife. It helps to make intercourse more than a mere physical sensation, as tender words are more than mere noise. Meaningful sex makes anyone, man or woman, feel wanted, needed, and loved in a deeply gratifying and comforting way.

Meaningful sex might be compared with a well-chosen Christmas present. When someone loves you enough to figure out something you would especially like, hunts around for it, spends his own money on it, wraps it up gaily, and gives it to you, you get a special thrill from the gift. If you buy the same article for yourself or get it from someone you don't care about, it gives you much less pleasure.

The difference is your emotional reaction to an expression of love. The same reaction, perhaps even more intense, generally comes with meaningful sex.

It would be naïve to identify meaningful sex entirely with faithful marriage. People use sex to express genuine love outside wedlock. They use sex as a mutual or contractual service to cement loveless marriage. Moreover, we could debate for days whether the extra pleasure and satisfaction gained through full emotional participation in one essentially constant relationship amounts in a lifetime to *more* or *less* than that gained through sexual experience with a variety of partners. Since no one person can follow both patterns, there is no way to settle the issue. My point is simply that although the extra pleasures of promiscuous sex can be readily scored and counted, meaningful sex in a constant relationship also gives substantial emotional benefits and intensified pleasures. These cannot be readily measured, and (like colors to a blind man) do not even seem to exist so far as those who do not enjoy them are concerned. But both husbands and wives get much more from a relationship in this setting than from mechanically conducted sexual services, however competent and varied they might be.

The other major issue on which new husbands and wives almost automatically differ concerns sex life control, and here the "male viewpoint" generally proves more beneficial.

Our ideas of feminine equality have changed rapidly in the past generation. However, there has been so little discussion, either public or private, of the specifics of husband-wife sex that no accepted approach has really been worked out. Everyone agrees that the concept of man the master and woman the slave is dead, but most men believe that it has been replaced by friendly cooperation (in which they get their way without having to throw their weight around), while many women believe they now have a perfect right to say "no" if they aren't in the mood.

Women definitely deserve equality. However, equality works in marriage only if you remember that you're talking about degree or quantity of benefits, not about qualitatively identical ones. An actress may be better known, better paid, and more respected than a policeman, but that doesn't qualify her to direct traffic. A woman's role in marriage can be just as important as a man's, she should have just as much stature and should get approximately equal satisfaction from it, but couple physiology demands that a wife yield—at least most of the time—to her husband's wishes regarding sex.

Many of the basic disagreements which arise with marriage center on these two issues. Even after years of marriage, many couples have never developed an understanding of each other's viewpoint, much less a way to resolve the differences. Would a discussion of "having sex" versus "making love" and "man the master" versus "equal rights for women" serve any purpose in your household? Even if you aren't aware of a disagreement on these matters, differing points of view may be contributing to apparently unrelated points of friction.

But let's not leave the impression that marriage only *creates* sexual problems. Sometimes it also *solves* them.

"Of course, I'm sure," Walter Kennedy said. "It's just that I don't believe in all these silly conventions. Neither does Peg. As long as we don't get caught with a pregnancy, we can't see any sense to getting married."

"That's right," Peg said. "I've seen it so many times: love and romance till you walk down the aisle—and fight, fight, fight from then on. Walt and I've been together five years now, and it's been peaches and cream all the way. Except for this sex thing. He's having more and more trouble with his erection, and I don't reach a climax as often as I should."

"Do you think your unconventional approach has anything to do with that?" I asked.

"Lord no," Walter said with a sardonic laugh. "What's the matter? Do we shock you or something?"

"I'm hard to shock. But what about you? Are you sure there isn't some remnant of conventionality deep inside that you're fighting all the time? You know, the attitudes you talk and think about play less part in emotional upheaval than the ones you never face."

"Save your time and our money, doc—there's nothing there. I've been that route till I'm sick of it, and there's nothing there."

"Then how about the unresolved issues involved? You're both against marriage, but for vastly different reasons. You're battling against conventionality, she's all for romance. Do those really add up to the same position?"

"Maybe, maybe not. But let's get down to our problem: my erections and her orgasms. What do you think we ought to do about that?"

"Why don't we start with a thorough physical check and a rundown on sex technique, because physical problems are easiest of all to correct and techniques often help a lot in just a visit or two. Deeper study of your male-female relationship or individual hang-ups always takes a lot longer."

"There's nothing wrong with either of us, and technique isn't the problem. But our male-female relationship —maybe you'll find something to help us with there."

Walter Kennedy didn't do anything I suggested the first time I suggested it, but he usually got around to it a visit or two later, when the initiative could be at least partially his. On the second visit I arranged physical checks and technique review sessions. These did not turn up simple solutions to the problems, but they did bring out at least one useful point.

As usual, I didn't wear gloves while pointing out the various spots that could be stimulated in sex play or intercourse. This omission was deliberate, as I have explained, to make the point that the sex organs are really clean. Peg remarked about this at the time, and said at a later visit:

"You know, all these years I've thought of my vagina as a nauseating kind of thing—don't look, don't touch, don't smell—but last night I got out the mirror and took a close look. It's sort of pretty, like a flower, with those pinkish folds and convolutions."

This conclusion did not help Peg to instant sexual success, but it removed one big roadblock. By the time we finished discussing the essential cleanness and rightness of sex in a proper framework, she felt much more comfortable about "all these things I used to believe were dirty or nasty."

Actually, this discussion also led us back into the subject of marriage. The "proper framework" expression did it; Walt picked me up on that in a hurry.

"What do you mean by 'proper'?" he asked. "Conventional, hidebound, temperance society style, after-the-priest-mumbles-the-formula matrimony?"

"Not quite." I laughed. "But perhaps a bit more stable and secure than what you've got now. The element of romance is fine, but where's the factor of commitment? Peg says you treat each other better than married folks who know their mates can't just pull out, but don't you treat each other better because of anxiety—because of uncertainty as to whether it will really last unless you make a special effort and because each of you doubts that the other loves you enough to stick with you through even one real fight? Maybe it makes things work out better in some ways than a solemn contract, but it also involves lots of doubt and uncertainty, plus a tendency to hang back from all-out emotional involvement."

"Nonsense!" Walter exclaimed. "You're just paying lip service to the usual drivel."

"Not really. Maybe the same behavior might ultimately result, but I'm not saying 'follow society's rules, set your conscience at rest and all will be well.' What I'm saying is that each of you needs a feeling of certainty and all-out commitment, right now and for some time to come, to get the most from your relationship. The traditional way of establishing that commitment is by marrying each other. It isn't necessarily the only way, but the approach you've used leaves long-range commitment out of the picture altogether."

"No, it doesn't. We love each other, we've loved each other for years, there's no reason for that to change."

I didn't answer, and after a pause we got off on other topics. But after a few weeks Peg and Walter sent me a note saying they were married, and that things were working out. A few months later I met Walter on the street.

"Funny thing," he said. "We fight more now that we're stuck with each other, but the problems we came to you about have disappeared. I still think we could have done it some other way, and I think we were standing up and being counted in the battle against enslavement by convention. But standing up and being counted as loving each other enough to make a lifelong contract has something to be said for it too, as long as you don't feel too much like a phony."

While some people enjoy the thrill of the chase and the excitement of romance, anxiety or uncertainty usually causes more trouble than benefit in a continuing relationship. Given relative certainty about your relationship's future, you can *both* care more, make love with less tension and anxiety, give each other greater rewards (which builds your worth in each other's eyes), and generally build a deeper relationship. Games of "chase me or romance me, then I'll give in" involve a constant need to measure up, constant anxiety, constant uncertainty. Marriage, whatever its faults, should eliminate these uncertainties. At least, it is the one reasonably binding way our society provides for saying "this is for keeps."

So whether it's a plus or a minus, marriage almost always changes a couple relationship profoundly. Short term or "on trial" courtship involves different behavior and different attitudes from those that apply after you make a lifelong commitment. You just cannot expect your man-woman relationship (especially with regard to sex) to remain the same.

4. Orgasm by Play Only

"It can't be Mary's fault," Jim Pearson said dejectedly, with his washed-gray eyes turned downward and his wiry hands in knots. "It's got to be me. I just can't get her over the top the natural way."

"What do you mean, the natural way?" I asked.

"By intercourse." He shifted disconcertedly in his chair. "No matter how I try, I just can't get her to come. But I know she's warm. There's nothing in the world wrong with the way she responds. So it's got to be me."

"She's interested and willing, then."

"That's right. And more—she has it, every way but when I'm inside."

"All the way through to a climax?"

"Sure. Sometimes two or three times before or after, but never the natural way. Not in eight years, not once."

"Let me make sure I understand. Your wife likes sex, you can excite her, and she has orgasm easily either before or after intercourse when you use your finger. But she never once has come during intercourse itself."

"That's right. Never when I'm inside. But she's so warm otherwise that it's got to be me."

"Not necessarily. Let's have her in and see what we can learn."

Mary Pearson entered my office forthrightly and sat down with complete composure. Jim introduced her deferentially, explaining (without being asked) that she was their town's chief librarian and that her responsibilities involved over a dozen people working under her. It was a revelation to see the way Jim's chest came out and his shoulders squared as Mary entered the room. His pride in her, and in the fact that she was his wife, seemed to suffuse him with a confidence he could never feel alone. Before either of them said a word, I began to understand why Jim had made a special effort to approach me first and take full blame: His wife could not be sullied and could have no faults.

"I've got good news for you," I said. "From what Jim tells me, I'm almost sure that I can help you. But before we cross a lot of bridges we might not even come to, let's check out the physical side of the situation."

A minute or so later, Mary had been set up for examination in the adjoining room, and the probable source of her difficulty showed up almost at first glance. While definitely normal, her inner lips and clitoris were located rather far forward, too far forward to be touched by a penis inserted straight into the vagina.

The true facts about the clitoris and feminine response are very hard to sort out from quackish pronouncements, psychiatric jargon, and misinterpretations. Even the best writings on the subject become distorted by the author's efforts to blast practices and ideas he feels are harmful and unsound. For example, some surgeons have performed operations to free the clitoris from surrounding scar tissue or to "uncover" it. Researchers who feel that such operations do more harm than good state strongly that immediate contact with the clitoris does not make any difference to a woman's response. Buried in the fine print of their reports, you will find reference to the clitoris as a crucial, sensitive structure which sexual friction ordinarily stimulates both directly and by the pulling and tugging of surrounding tissues. But because of the author's surgery-fighting emphasis, the headlines make it seem that the clitoris has been proved unimportant.

As another example, psychiatrists who concern themselves mainly with emotional response to sex and never touch or look at their clients' organs often talk about "clitorine" as opposed to "vaginal" orgasm. The meaning they assign to these terms has nothing to do with the exact spot being stimulated when orgasm occurs. A "vaginal" orgasm in this context is one which occurs at the conclusion of meaningful lovemaking in which both partners regard their caresses and actions as gestures of deep affection. A "clitorine" one results from physical manipulation without such love values, whether through masturbation or through sexual stimulation by a man for whom the woman has no real feeling and whether the stimulation comes from a finger on the clitoris or a penis far inside.

These ideas, then, basically involve the emotional frame-work in which the stimulations occur, not their site. But many people who have heard these terms do not under-stand this fact, so Masters and Johnson (in *Human Sexual Response*) made a big point of the fact that the physical changes of orgasm are the same no matter what type of stimulation causes it. This statement has now been misin-terpreted further as "all orgasms are the same." Since Masters and Johnson clearly state that they did not ap-praise the emotional element, such a conclusion cannot be warranted. The stress on "vaginal" and "clitorine" being identical has also been misinterpreted as proof that the clitoris is unimportant, with any genital stimulation equivalent to any other.

In my opinion, direct friction and pressure on the clitoris itself is not necessary for feminine response, but direct or transmitted stimulation in the area is an im-portant, and sometimes indispensable, excitement source.

"Here's your clitoris," I said to Mary after a complete examination had showed no further problems, "and here's the direction in which your vagina runs. There's nothing wrong or abnormal about either, but it just happens that the straight-in path to the vagina doesn't come even close to the clitoris or inner lips."

"And that's the whole trouble?" Mary asked.

"It might well be. Of course, two or more factors often enter into sexual difficulties, so there's no guarantee that steps to correct this situation will solve your whole prob-lem. But there's a very good chance."

"What do I do, then?"

"Try sex in positions that bring the penis into better contact with your organ's front rim. Let's get Jim in here for a minute, and I'll explain it to you."

Before we get into the cure, let's discuss the diagnosis a bit more. Orgasm by play only is one of the commonest sex problems, and it is easy for any woman to check herself for anatomical causes.

Use a tampon inserter to represent a penis. Place the inserter in the vagina and take a look. Bear in mind that sexual excitement generally doubles the thickness of the inner lips and that if the inner lips are in the action path they will cause enough tugging on the clitoris to stimulate it even if it is beyond the range of actual friction. But if intercourse with the penis directed straight into the vagina will miss the inner lips and clitoris by half an inch or more, the special postures and techniques described below might prove worthwhile.

Actually, even if you have completely normal genital contours, which is the case with about half those who achieve orgasm by play only, there is a good chance that special postures and techniques will prove helpful. Nobody really knows what causes some women to get less stimulation than others from sexual friction at the vagina's front rim, but the fact remains that many women with quite ordinary genital contours rely on play for their orgasms, and that most of them respond to the program originally devised to make up for a high clitoris or small inner lips.

"Mary's organs are perfectly normal," I said to Jim when he came into the examining room. "But her particular contours make it hard for the frictions of ordinary intercourse to reach the clitoris area. She gets to a climax easily in play because your finger rubs the right area, but she can't during intercourse because the penis always misses it."

I moved slightly so that Jim could see the organs themselves, spread the outer lips to get them out of the way, and pointed out the junction of the inner lips at the front corner.

"Right here is the important spot. The clitoris itself lies just above and in front of this junction—you can see it pop from under my finger when I roll it across here. The clitoris gets bigger and firmer with sexual excitement, but not big enough to make up for its out-of-the-way location. Fortunately, you don't have to touch the clitoris itself to cause a climax. In fact, the clitoris normally pulls back and changes shape just before orgasm anyway, so that almost no one rubs it directly all the way to the conclusion. The inner lips pull and tug on the clitoris to stimulate it whether or not you actually hit the exact spot."

While holding the outer lips apart with my left hand, I put my right index finger into the vagina itself.

"Now here's where Mary's problem starts," I said. "She happens to be built in such a way that none of the front rim structures—neither her clitoris nor her inner lips—reach down into the action path. So in the usual sex position she gets very little stimulation of the clitoris either by pressure and friction or by pulling and tugging. The whole area just gets left out during intercourse itself, even though it's well in range of finger caress."

"Is that so important? Aren't there other sensitive areas, too?"

"There will be, after Mary has orgasm during intercourse a few times. But the other areas have to pick up sexual sensitivity by being stimulated during keen excitement. You know how it was with Pavlov's dogs. At first they only salivated when food was in their mouths, but then he rang a bell every time they had food, and after a while the bell alone would make them drool. It's the same way with a woman. At first, she needs strong stimulation at the front rim of the vagina to reach a climax. After a number of fully successful episodes, any of the stimulations she usually gets in the process, from motion of the penis in the vagina to preliminary breast caresses, can set her off. But her early orgasms all start here, at the front rim of her sex organ."

"Then the other areas will get sensitive later?"

"Usually, if Mary gets a climax during intercourse a few times through the measures I'm going to suggest. Most patients find that they need to use special positions and techniques only for a few weeks or months, after which nerve fibers in other areas become sexually attuned and stimulation of the clitoris area itself becomes unnecessary. Which fits in with what doctors have known for years: that removing the clitoris before successful sex adjustment makes a woman permanently frigid, while removing it after she has become fully responsive usually has absolutely no effect. So if you succeed a few times through the special techniques I'm going to teach you, Mary will probably respond to any normal approach thereafter."

"Exactly what are we supposed to do?" Jim asked.

"First, try sex postures which bring the top of the penis into firmer contact with the front rim of the vagina. If you look at my finger here, you'll see that there are two basic ways to do this: You can change the *angle* at which you enter, so that you go more or less from front corner to rear depths instead of straight along the path. Or you can keep at the same angle and push your whole body up toward the head of the bed, so that the top of the penis presses against the front rim structures like this."

Jim nodded.

"Take a good look first at the exact angle the vagina lies in now, with Mary's legs up in something similar to their position during ordinary intercourse. Now look what happens when she lets one leg down; as her thigh gets close to the table, it tips her pelvis backward a bit. If you stay in the same relative position, this changes your angle of entry to make it more front-to-back than straight in."

"I can see that, but I don't see how I can stay in the same position."

"Actually, you probably won't. You partly straddle the leg she has down straight. But that shifts *you* in the right direction, too. It brings the penis in still more front to back, and makes for extra pressure and friction at the vagina's front rim. Now let's see what happens with both Mary's legs down—the angle of entry becomes even more favorable, and with your legs on the outside you will find that it works very well. Your weight helps hold her thighs down tight against the bed without either of you making any effort at all. Her organs are tipped and your angle of entry altered in such a way that the top of the penis's shaft comes into much firmer contact with the clitoris and inner lips."

"But doesn't that leave sort of a narrow passage? I don't know whether I can get in like that."

"You're right. Most couples make entrance with one or both of the wife's legs spread, then change into this posture after they're already joined."

"And that's the whole business? You think sex in this position might do the trick?"

"It should definitely help. But there are a couple of other things you can try. Before we go into them, though, I want to make sure that you understand what we've been through so far. We're trying to bring your penis into the vagina at more of an angle, so that its shaft rubs along the front rim of Mary's organ while its tip rubs along the back wall. One way to do that is to tip her pelvis back, and having one or both legs down straight on the bed usually accomplishes that goal. So you can put one of your legs on top of one of hers, which still leaves you plenty of room to make entrance and leaves her one leg in good position for sexual movement. Or you can make your entrance first, then let her put both legs down straight while you straddle her thighs, which brings you in from a sharp angle above and usually puts peak pressure on the front rim area. You'll find that all of these positions snug up vaginal contact a bit, so you have to take it a bit easy on sex movement at first to keep from losing control. It is sudden change in excitement that tips a man into premature climax, but longer, more intense sex play will actually help. Genital caresses are especially important, Mary, and I'll tell you exactly where you can do what in a little while.* Just be extra sure that Jim is at a peak of excitement before you start intercourse in these positions. Otherwise, the snugger fit might make him a bit too fast for you."

"Will it be snug enough that it might hurt us?" Mary asked.

"Not now. These positions don't work too well for beginners because the penis comes in at such an angle that a virgin or near-virgin finds it uncomfortable. The extra snugness makes it hard for an inexperienced husband to control himself, too. But by the time you've been married for a year or so, and particularly after you've had a child, there's plenty of room at any angle and control should be no problem.

"The next position I want to teach you is exactly the same with Mary on top. You might not find it the best way after you get started, but it's often a very good way to try once or twice. In this position, Mary can move in different ways until she finds what works best. Then both of you will get some idea of what angle the penis should come in

* See Chapter Two.

at, how much it takes in the way of pressure against the front rim of the vagina to give stimulation, and how much pressure Mary can stand without discomfort (both a lot more than you expect). Some of my patients find this position extremely satisfying, but most couples find that the woman gets tired if she has to make virtually all the movement."

"We tried it with me on top when we first started," Mary said. "It didn't seem to do much for me then."

"With your legs together in between his?"

"No, my legs were spread and I sort of sat on him."

I nodded. "That's the way most couples do it with the wife on top. With your legs spread, you usually have to keep your body almost straight up to keep your thighs from hitting his hip bones and holding him out of range. When your body is almost perpendicular to his, the front rim of your female organ stays way out of contact.

"You have to put your legs down straight between Jim's and let your whole body rest upon him to get good front rim contact. You can move by pushing off with your toes or knees so that your whole body moves lengthwise, or you can slide down toward the foot of the bed a bit to press the front rim of your organ against the top of the penis and rock your pelvis to get movement. But rock your hips *away from* Jim instead of *toward* him. That gives extra front rim friction.

"You won't get anywhere by mimicking Jim's normal actions. That's the one action which won't do a thing for you, because if you rock forward the way he does during each thrust the tipping of your hips will put your organ's front rim structures out of range again. But experiment with different positions and motions until you find what gives you the kind of stimulation you've been getting from play. When you get in good contact, you'll be able to make the frictions just as heavy or just as light as you want them. You can go entirely by feel—whatever stimulates you without causing discomfort is fine."

"And I can't do much when we try it that way?" Jim asked.

"You can make ordinary rocking motions to some extent, just as your wife does when she's on bottom with her legs spread. You'll find it's easy to do as long as she just lets herself rest on you all the way so that most of her weight is on your chest instead of crushing your hips (as it does in the usual wife-on-top position). Incidentally, I don't want her to hold up her weight on her elbows or arms the way you do, because your angle of entry is more apt to be right if her upper body is right down on top of you than if it's raised.

"There's one other way for you to increase sex movement in this position. If Mary rests her full length right down on you, you'll find that there's enough elasticity in your tissues that you can slide her up and down very easily with your hands. The fat underneath your two layers of skin acts just like ball bearings as long as the movement doesn't overstretch it. Just grasp her hips from the side and move her any way you want without lifting her."

Jim and Mary both nodded.

"Now let's get on to a different approach." I turned to Mary. "Instead of tipping the pelvis by pulling your legs down, let's try tipping it by increasing the curvature of your low back. Just exaggerate the hollow of your low back for a moment. There—see how the front rim of her female organ tips down closer to the action path? Obviously, Mary can't hold that position long without support, but if she puts a pillow or a rolled sheet underneath the arch of her back it will automatically tip her organs into a more favorable position. You can use this pillow trick to modify the ordinary man-on-top woman's-legs-spread posture and greatly increase stimulation of the clitoris. Only be sure to keep the pillow up under the low back instead of under the hips."

"And I just do things the same as always?" Jim asked.

"More or less. Either the pillow trick or the legs-down posture might tip Mary's organs at a sufficient angle to shift sexual friction to the front rim where she needs it. But there's one step you can take in either posture to help. Let me show you how it works."

I placed one finger into Mary's vagina, lined up directly with its canal.

"Here's the position you've been in before, with the penis missing the front rim altogether."

I tipped the finger at exactly the same angle and pressed it snugger against the front rim.

"Here's what you can do to help. If you're in a position that makes your angle of entry favorable, you will exert much more pressure and friction on the key spots if you move your body an inch or two toward the head of the bed. When you have a firm erection, you'll find that you can press down on the base of the shaft with almost all your might without any discomfort because of its strong attachments. So if you get well into the vagina then slide your whole body toward the head of the bed, you can put the base of your penis into firm contact with Mary's inner lips and possibly with the clitoris itself. In Mary's case, this won't work in the ordinary legs-spread-and-low-back-posture because you would press against the top wall of the vagina instead of the female organ's front rim. But if she either has her legs down or her low back arched, her clitoris and inner lips will be just above your penis and the headward slide will stimulate her quite strongly."

"Then I just push my whole body up toward the top of

the bed so that the top of my penis stays snug against her organs and move in the usual way?"

"Most of the time, yes. But if you start to get ahead of her, there's one other action which might help. Push all the way in, keeping the top of the penis firm against her, and rock your hips from side to side. This won't push you toward a climax the way in-and-out movement will, but it may give enough rolling-pin-style friction against the clitoris and inner lips to help Mary."

"And I move as usual?" Mary asked.

"Yes. Of course, you won't be able to move much if you have both legs down straight. Otherwise you can do whatever you please.

"One further point. Mary can probably reach a second or third climax easier and faster than a first, so try prolonging sex play beforehand until she has at least one orgasm. She will probably have to caress your genitals rather actively to keep you at full excitement."

"And that's the whole story?"

"Just about. Since you've found that Mary is so very responsive in sex play, I'm almost sure that you'll have success with the both-legs-down posture, combined with the headward slide. You might need to learn how much pressure gives her the most stimulation by letting her on top with her legs between yours and her body down level with yours. The pillow trick and the one-leg-down postures should allow mutual movement and extra variety without losing front rim friction. And I really expect that you'll be able to enjoy almost any sex posture, even those that put the front rim completely out of range, after two or three months at most.

"There is one more step you can take, though, if you give these measures a fair trial and they don't quite work. I've had a few patients who couldn't get quite enough front rim friction to reach a climax with the measures I've suggested. One had an abnormally small clitoris and had to take hormone treatment to enlarge it before she reached orgasm even in play. A few others seemed normal but needed a lot more stimulation than Mary does. Some had not been married very long and had not had children, so that their organs were still too snug for sex postures which bring the penis into the vagina at a sharp angle. In some of these cases, finger stimulation of the clitoris area during intercourse proved helpful. The wife would lie on her side, the husband insert his penis from the rear. He would lie quietly, with just enough movement to keep his erection, and simultaneously play her past a climax with his hand. It's a much less satisfying approach than the more direct one, though, and I would keep it as a last resort."

Actually, last resorts proved unnecessary for the Pearsons. Jim telephoned the very next day to say that Mary had reached a climax "the natural way," and that they were both delighted. About three months later I had a note from them saying that sex in normal postures was working fine, and that their problem seemed entirely solved. Not all cases come out this well, but enough have success to make the program worth a try in any case of orgasm by play only.

5. The Frigid Woman

"I don't think I've ever had a climax," Frieda Shiller said. "But how do you tell?"

Frieda had come in to discuss her "frigidity." Her own doctor had examined her thoroughly before sending her to me and had eliminated physical disorders. We were having a private interview before we brought her husband into the picture.

"You feel waves of physical pleasure," I said, "which start in the genitals and spread through the body. Then you get a feeling of peaceful contentment. The details vary a lot, but there never seems to be much doubt when it happens."

"No, I've never had anything like that," Frieda said. "Not that I think sex is awful or anything, but if I get stirred up it just goes about so far and then I lose it. I don't get left high, it just goes flat and I don't want any more. It's really easier on me if I don't get involved, but every now and then I've got to try to make it really right."

"Right for whom?"

"Right for both of us, I guess. But especially for Herman. If I can't get anything out of sex that's my punishment for *my* fault, and I can live with it if I have to. But what really bothers me is that I'm shortchanging Herman. He's been so good to me, but I just can't come with him like I should."

Why do frigid women almost always feel ashamed? Their condition is not of their own making. It victimizes *them*, not others. But guilt almost always accompanies "coldness," adding greatly to its discomfiture. My first objective in talking with Frieda Shiller was to relieve this feeling, so that at least she would find her affliction easier to live with while we tried to correct it.

"Doesn't Herman get any satisfaction?" I asked.

"He says so. But I'm sure it would be better for him if I could respond. Everybody says that you only get the real thing when you both reach a climax."

"That's not quite right. It's true that you *share* feelings of pleasure when you're in love, so that sex-spurred emotion builds up by echoing back and forth between you. But the feeling that a woman loves him enough to please him without having anything to gain herself means something to a man, too. And the physical sensations a man gets during intercourse doesn't change a whole lot whether the woman has a climax or not, if she's really doing her best for him. In fact, the shoe may even be on the other foot."

"What do you mean?"

"You can bring your husband at least as much pleasure by trying deliberately to please him as you would by having a climax. It's true that most women move more and caress their husbands more when they themselves are aroused, but it doesn't have to be that way. In fact, the famed courtesans at the French royal courts used to avoid having a climax with their patrons because they could be much more pleasing by deliberate sexual maneuver than by instinct."

"But I thought there was more to it than that. Wouldn't there be some kind of changes in my organs that gave him a special thrill?"

"*Changes* yes, *special thrills* no. Your vagina contracts in rhythmic waves during an orgasm, which has the effect during intercourse of making rings of snugness run up the penis. But these movements are sufficiently gentle that their effect is largely lost in the vaster frictions of sexual movement. Perhaps if you were perfectly still the vaginal movement of your orgasm would give your husband some sensations he wouldn't otherwise receive, but not if both of you are moving."

"So I can please Herman just as much whether I reach a climax or not?"

"That's right. And you can be just as good a woman."

"A woman?"

I nodded.

"I know the notion of equality of the sexes has somehow been twisted around to make orgasms the test of a woman's sexual powers these days, the way they are for a man. But this idea doesn't make sense when you examine it. Your husband has to get excited about you sexually before you can have intercourse, but the shoe is on the other foot with you. All you have to do is get him excited, not get excited yourself. Your husband has to go all the way to a conclusion before he calls himself a man, but you can be a successful woman just by satisfying *him* whether or not you get any passionate satisfaction yourself."

"But isn't it natural to have a climax?"

"And unnatural—in other words, bad—not to have one? What would your grandmother say about that? In her day (and even today in one New England state with rather backward laws) a woman could be put in jail for disgracing the marriage bed with lustful passions. Feminine orgasm was the Devil's bait—temptation to fleshly excess. Even your mother didn't anticipate much in the way of orgasm. By her generation, most people looked on passion as proper and Godly in marriage, but sex was still 'the husband's privilege.' Were all the generations before this one, then, unnatural freaks? I hardly think so. Sex with mutual orgasm gives extra satisfaction and helps to make a marriage closer, so it's a worthwhile end to strive toward. But it's far, far from being the 'natural' way, and you shouldn't think less of yourself for having had trouble achieving it."

"But *why* haven't I achieved it? Herman and I love each other. We get along all right in every other way. Why can't I build up to that special point?"

"Let's see whether we can find out."

We went over a lot of background material then, without finding much of help. Frieda could recall no causes of unpleasant associations with sex. She had never been raped; her introduction to intercourse had been both gentle and considerate. She had been trained to fear strange men as had most girls, but did not seem to have taken this association too seriously. Her parents had not discussed sex with her, and no one seems to have filled her with the prohibitions and taboos which so many girls find hard to get rid of after marriage. Modesty may have been slightly overstressed—she could not recall having seen her mother nude, much less her father—but she participated in sex play without requiring total darkness and showed no hesitation about self-exposure with her husband.

It was when we discussed her relations as a child with her parents that we learned several significant points.

"You mean that as a woman you feel free to expose yourself to Herman, but as a child you didn't feel free to expose yourself to your father?"

Frieda looked somewhat puzzled.

"Of course," she said.

"Don't you see any connection?"

"No. Herman's Herman and Dad's Dad."

"Most people find the patterns they develop with their parents applying to some extent in marriage. Particularly where intimate relations are concerned—you sort of rehearse deep emotional attachments and constant togetherness in the family."

"Maybe. But my folks didn't show much feeling. Not for me or for each other, when you come right down to it."

"What do you mean?"

"They had things worked out between them so there wasn't any fuss. Dad brought home the money, Mom took care of the kids and the house. I never heard them argue, but I never saw them kiss. My father used to hold mother's coat and open the door when they went out; he'd carry the groceries for her and sit next to her in church, but I never saw him touch her on purpose in his life, or she him. They got along just fine, but it was an *arrangement* not a *relationship*, if you know what I mean."

"And where did you fit in?"

"As part of the place, like the furniture or the oven I guess. They did everything for me, all right. I had clothes and spending money, the meals were good, they sent me to school and helped me with my lessons. But I can't remember any gesture of affection."

To a woman, sex is generally a super-caress, a physical intimacy which simultaneously measures, builds, and celebrates the ties of love. The physical sensations of sexual contact do not bring pleasure at first. They need to be linked with fulfilling emotion, either directly or indirectly (and either by personal experience or by communication).

Most people do not realize how indirect and vague an association can link an idea or act and a given emotion. Like fuzzballs moving in the wind, various notions tangle with each other in your brain whenever they get even close. An infant gets food at the same time he is being held, for instance, and the pleasure of satisfying hunger links itself in his mind with physical contact. This experience is far removed from intercourse, yet there is good reason to believe that it plays an important part in later sexual adjustment.*

Even emotions which have no relationship whatever to given ideas or acts except for similar settings or names may be linked to those ideas and acts later. This is the root of many inhibitions—feelings of guilt, shame, or fear linked illogically with self-exposure, sex play, or intercourse. Most of all, the feeling you get for other people in one form of intimacy often springs into your breast when you encounter remotely similar circumstances in another. A girl who has enjoyed a loving and fulfilling relationship

---

* Baby monkeys fed in such a way that they have no contact with soft or skinlike surfaces are unable to mate comfortably as adults. Baby monkeys fed in the same way, but with a skinlike surface simultaneously presented to their touch, have a normal sex life.

with her father can "fall in love at first sight" with a man who reminds her of him (perhaps in manner, movement, scent, skin texture, or ways other than appearance). She can respond to him as a total person, including his sexuality and his physical expressions of it, much more readily than a girl without these head-start linkages of pleasant emotions with her man.

A great many women establish full responsiveness without this head start. They have not been cuddled or caressed as young girls, or demonstratively loved as adolescents. But most of them have at least been aware of a loving man-woman relationship near by. A girl who does not experience demonstrative (but perfectly proper) love from her father can still be keenly aware of his love for her mother and of her mother's response to it. Youngsters share so keenly the emotions of those they love that such experience almost matches personal contact in its ability to build later responsiveness. In fact, girls who share the same household with a loving, fairly demonstrative couple during their early childhood seldom have difficulty developing sexual response whether said couple are parents, siblings, or unrelated boarders.

If, like Frieda Shiller, you are a woman who has had none of these opportunities, you still have some hope of building responsiveness. Let's go back to Frieda Shiller's case to see how this process works. We'll pick up the story during a later interview, with both Herman and Frieda present.

"So it's not my fault that I'm like this," Frieda said. "Maybe that's right, and maybe it's an extra reason for trying to get straightened out. God knows I don't want my girls to have to go through this. But how does it help me to know where my trouble started?"

"Maybe it doesn't, in your case. If you had had a bad experience—if you had gotten mixed up somehow in your relations with your father or mother, or if you had suffered great fright or shame in connection with sex at an earlier age—reliving the experience through conversation might help you to sort things out. But when the problem is a *lack*, not a foul-up, we're left with a big void which you and Herman have to fill."

"But Herman's been so considerate. I don't see how he could do any more."

"Maybe he needs to be a little less considerate," I said. "Maybe even a lot less considerate."

"What do you mean?"

"It's awfully easy for a man to try so hard to be nice—constantly asking his wife whether what he is doing is all right and whether she is ready for the next step—that he winds up being almost namby-pamby.

"A woman should *respond* sexually, which means that she has to have something she can respond *to*. If the man works too hard at being considerate, he never gives his wife an assertive figure with whom she can have a natural feminine relationship."

"You mean just go ahead when she doesn't want to?" Herman asked. "Wouldn't that hurt her and set everything back?"

"Not necessarily. Sure, it's possible to be a brute and turn sex into a nightmare. But we're not talking about legalized rape, we're talking about assertive, lovingly masterful masculinity. That's what the honeymoon, of which most people have such unrealistic expectations, is all about. Even a woman with ideal emotional upbringing gets no real physical pleasure from early intercourse. She gets a feeling of fulfillment at having pleased her husband; she feels pleasure in his pleasure and these plus emotions add to the others she has linked with close man-woman contact until the total emotional color attached to intercourse results in a climax. The key point is that *his satisfaction* leads to *hers*—that her feeling of fulfillment comes from having given pleasure, not from having received it, and her feeling of empathic enjoyment comes from an appreciation of the feelings in his breast, not from surges of feeling originating in her own."

"You mean the woman's pleasure always lags behind the man's?" Frieda asked.

"Lags behind it, and to a great extent at first results from it. That's why your program for straightening out the situation has to involve both of you, and perhaps him even more than yourself."

"Me?" Herman asked.

"Yes, we're going to have to roll back the clock to the honeymoon phase and fill in a gap in your couple development. Look at it this way. Early in your relationship, you should have enjoyed sex contact with Frieda. Her awareness of your pleasure should have given her pleasure, both because she was fulfilling her role as a wife and because love let her share your emotion. But for a variety of reasons this didn't happen often enough or intensely enough. You got too worried and anxious to enjoy it. She started to fret about whether she was normal. You became self-conscious about pleasing yourself at her expense and started to bottle up any expression of pleasure. She turned her eyes inward looking for some spark she could fan into an orgasm instead of directing her attentions toward you and your responses. Something interfered with your pleasure, her awareness of it, or your mutual relationship."

"But how can we straighten things out?" Frieda asked.

"First, take it by stages. You're in the position where most couples start their sex lives: a man ready to enjoy sex, a woman willing to tolerate it for the sake of couple welfare or future prospects, and some bonds of love between you. Don't expect results in a hurry just because you've been married for several years. It may take just as long to renovate your sex life as it would have to build. What you need is to put it on a basis where you can both be comfortable while you wait, patiently, for further developments."

I turned to Herman.

"Second," I said. "Approach sex strictly for your own fun. Remember, the only way Frieda will ever react is by awareness of your pleasure. If you can't enjoy yourself at her expense for the moment, she'll never have a chance to link pleasurable emotions with sex. So long-range considerateness requires you to be a bit of a bastard now, by which I mean that you should take sex when you want it without worrying about whether Frieda is in the mood, carry through the act as slowly or as rapidly as you find most pleasurable, and enjoy it without any feeling of guilt, shame, or hesitation because she hasn't caught up to you. Of course it's possible to carry being a bastard too far—to insist on sex while the dinner burns or on intercourse without lubrication—but since you've leaned over backward to be considerate for years I'm sure that you couldn't do these things if you tried. So just be selfish, do everything you can think of to enjoy yourself in bed, and in the long run you'll both be better off for it."

During this discourse, Herman looked doubtful and hesitant. But Frieda kept nodding, and it was she who spoke.

"That's right," she said. "Sometimes I've felt just on the verge, when he's asked me: 'Think you're getting ready?' or 'Is it all right if I go on?' and it just curdles inside me."

"Remember that," I told Herman. "Don't ever ask a

question. I'll tell you how to find the answers for yourself, so far as Frieda's state of sexual excitement is concerned.* But in bed right now you need to be the master, the leader, the firm figure to whom Frieda can respond."

"Well, I guess I can take what I want, if that's the only way."

"That's part of it. You've got to enjoy yourself, to put your own pleasure on the top of your list, to run the show to suit yourself. And you've got to feel one hundred percent comfortable about it. As long as you feel the least twinge of shame or guilt or concern about what you're putting Frieda through, your pleasure won't come through to her. So you've got not only to *feel* pleasure, but to *feel it in a context that lets you share it with your wife.* As long as you feel the least bit anxious or unsure, she will share your anxiety and doubt instead of your pleasure."

"That sounds sort of mystical."

"Fair enough—it *is* sort of mystical. Like anything to do with the emotional side of making love, nobody really knows *how* it happens, just that it does. I've always explained personal relationships in terms of shared feelings. You're an *acquaintance* when you have some idea of what the other fellow is feeling. You move up to *friendship* when his joys and sorrows come through to you and affect your own emotional state. You *identify* with him when the things that happen to him affect not only your emotions but your pride—when *you* become ashamed if *he* gets caught off base, or *you* puff up your breast when *he* hits a home run. And that kind of relationship, added to the joy and security and pride of having achieved it, constitutes love.

"Family ties or marriage aid identification. You share the same name, reputation, and circumstances. But it still

* By the nipple, clitoris, and vaginal moisture changes described in Chapter Two.

takes moments of real closeness, without the need to defend yourself in any way from one another, to make it work. And that's the kind of moment you have to create in the course of sexual intercourse to get an emotional spiral building between you.

"Mystical, yes. But not so strange or unfamiliar, if you think about other moments of real closeness you've enjoyed."

At this point, Frieda and Herman talked about their experiences, with each other and with their parents or friends. It was a good discussion, and one which made the points we were discussing definitely clearer. Its benefits came mainly from flashes of feeling, though, not from words or ideas which I can set down here. Herman said something like "Remember that time at Harriet's?" and they both whooped with laughter. "And the time you came home looking like you'd just been fired or something." Frieda said, "I don't even remember what happened to who, but I was so worried!" Herman nodded, looking at her tenderly.

Meaningful moments between people in love seem either maudlin or mysterious to strangers, so even if I knew the details I would not record them. Take a few minutes, though, to recollect moments from your own life. Have you shared joy or sorrow? Have you felt ashamed of someone else's act? Have you been proud of something someone else (whether a member of your family, your school team, or your community) achieved? Then you have belonged to something, and belonging to a person in sound marriage is one step closer as a result.

"I understand," Frieda said. "He has to enjoy himself and be at ease."

"And so do you," I said. "Be at ease, that is. Sex in this

framework shouldn't hurt. Herman will see to that. But Herman can't keep you from feeling ashamed or resentful or anxious, and those feelings will block the kind of emotional exchange we're discussing. It's easy for a woman to feel used or abused or belittled in sex. After all, you've heard the term 'screwed' and its four-letter equivalents a thousand times in a sense which demeans the woman's role. People don't really mean to connect these words with married love—they signify physical lust without love—but the demeaning connotations link themselves with female sex in almost every mind, and stay attached at some level below the conscious."

"You mean that I resent being made love to?"

"Would you resent being 'fucked' or 'screwed?' The actions are the same, only the connotations differ. And your mind ties all these fuzzballs in one package—all the related ideas and terms and acts, from the historical fact that marriage makes the wife a chattel to the everyday allusion that makes a person who is screwed a laughing-stock. Maybe if we talked for a month we could uproot most of those feelings, but there is a quicker, easier way. You don't have to tear your bad associations out by the roots if you can overwhelm them with new good ones. This plan will work, if you can keep from resenting Herman's having fun with you and realize that it isn't *at your expense* but *for your sake*. Just remember that you're both trying in a different way to build something between you as a couple and that as a couple, for both your sakes, you need to open up to each other completely without barriers of shame or resentment or inadequacy or fear."

Once again, we examined these ideas at length. Frieda recalled the times she had heard words like "fucked," "screwed," "had his fun with her," and so forth, and the

demeaning snickers that went with them. "Those notions sure make a woman's part in sex seem low," she said.
Search your own memory for similar experiences. How
many times have you heard someone refer to a woman's
role in sex? Were any of those references admiring or re-
spectful, or even neutral in their tone? If so, how many—
one tenth, one hundredth, one thousandth or less? Yet you
expect to go to bed in marriage, either as a husband or a
wife, and suddenly deem the woman's role in sex wholly
respectable, wholly admirable, a sound basis for sexual
and personal pride! Search your own history, and cast
searching light upon these memories, because without that
light they will always plague you.

"Let's finish on a more homely note," I said to Frieda.
"Most experts have found that any time you have an
orgasm, no matter how you got to it, you sort of break a
barrier so that you get the next one much more easily.
So there's one further step you yourself can take: You can
try forms of sex play which stimulate the front corner of
the female organ very strongly, and see whether these
methods help you reach a climax. This isn't meant as a
substitute for Herman's attentions, but simply as a way
of taking advantage of sex urges that might arise when he
isn't around, or of detouring the roadblocks that come up
when you're with him. If you feel sexually responsive,
don't hesitate to play yourself past a climax if you possibly
can. One team of sex experts even asks patients to keep a
hand vibrator around—one of those motors with an out-
of-balance wheel that barbers or masseurs hook on the
backs of their hands to make their fingers quiver firmly.
You can stimulate the clitoris and inner lips more strongly
by using one of these than in any other way I know. But
be careful of long fingernails—either trim them or keep

them away from tender tissues—and use plenty of K-Y or other jelly for lubrication."

I turned to Herman.

"Of course," I said, "you can use a vibrator, too, if you want. Whenever you both feel as if the mood gives you a chance, there's no reason not to try for feminine orgasm as long as you don't strain for it. Nothing in the rules says the first time has to be with the penis in place, and lots of women who can't manipulate themselves into orgasm can relax completely if their husbands help them."

"And that's a help instead of hindrance?" Herman asked.

"Anything you do for each other is a help, as long as it's a road toward improved lovemaking rather than a substitute for married sex. Masturbation or playing past a climax are neither right nor wrong by themselves. They're right as long as you make them servants to improved couple sex life, and wrong if you let them interfere."

I suppose that if Frieda and Herman had been of different religious conviction, I might have encountered sharp resistance to the idea of generating a climax by any possible means (even though the ultimate aim was to generate one through the making of love). They were of liberal persuasion, though, and the idea sat just as well as any. I don't know the exact technique they used, or whether it contributed to their success. I only know what Herman reported a year or so later that Frieda was enjoying orgasm fairly often, both in preliminary play (specifically without a vibrator at this point) and in intercourse. Strangely enough, this isn't what interested me the most. The really fascinating story Herman told had to do with his ten-year-old son.

"Jim's friend had him on the phone when I got home," Herman said. "They were talking about a camping trip, and Frieda was right there. I could tell by her manner that she didn't much approve, and I'm sure Jim knew the way she felt about it, too. He was sort of avoiding her eyes and stalling. Then when I pushed open the door, he said into the phone: 'Just a minute, Dad's here. Just let me tell him about it, and he'll say either 'yes' or 'no.' ' "

Herman told that story with great pride and I felt deeply proud, too. Not only because he had become master of his own house, but because he recognized exactly what had happened, and how, and why.

6. Potency Fears

"Maybe it's all over for me," Bob Metcalf said. "But I'd like to be sure."

"Sure of what?" I asked.

"That I'm too old for sex. You may say there's nothing to be done. But I've got to be sure there's no way to get my powers back."

"How old are you, anyway?"

"Forty-seven."

He shook his head.

"Better tell me just what happened," I said. "How long since everything was right for you?"

"Up until four or five months ago. Till then everything

was perfect. Then one night I got started, and when the crucial moment came my penis just wasn't hard. I felt excited enough and eager, and I figured it would be all right if I could just get inside. So I guided it in with my fingers, and it was just firm enough to move back and forth. It never did get hard, though. After a while I had a climax, but it never got hard." Bob paused to wipe the sweat off his palms. "Believe me, I felt real upset—that's the first time in my life I ever had trouble. So the next time I was clutched up and anxious, and it didn't go well at all. Then once or twice it went fair, but not like it used to be. And here lately I can't even get started—Ruth starts and I just freeze inside."

"And you think it might be your age?"

"Sure. I'm forty-seven. If I'm all worn out I'll try to live with it, but I've got to be sure there's nothing left."

The "male menopause" is a perfect example of the self-fulfilling prophesy: an otherwise unfounded myth which makes itself true through belief in it. Age alone does not make a man impotent. Almost half the men in their eighties who have a willing partner can manage intercourse, and who knows how many others could if they had the confidence to try? Yet any man over forty-five who fails to get an erection thinks he is over the hill. His conviction that old age has caught up with him shakes his confidence and itself impairs his potency. Often a problem that would otherwise correct itself in a few weeks causes permanently crippling emotional aftermaths: The man just doesn't try sex any more, or he frets so much that his anxieties themselves make him impotent. And if his problem stems from some simply corrected difficulty, he doesn't find the cure because he doesn't look for it. He just blames old age.

"I'll tell you this much right now," I told Bob Metcalf. "You're not impotent from age alone at forty-seven. But the first thing we have to settle is whether there's any physical disorder involved. You haven't any urge at all to have sex these days, right?"

"Right."

"What about dreams? Do you have any erotic dreams, or wake up at night with an erection?"

"No, not lately."

"Any so-called 'bladder erections'? When you wake up in the morning with a full bladder, do you ever have an erection which subsides when you start to void?"

"No. That used to happen to me all the time, but not for the past three or four months."

"And never during sex play or masturbation or anything of that kind?"

"Of course not—nothing like that."

"No erections at all, across the board—in dreams, in the morning, with sex play, or with self-stimulation?"

"Right."

"In that case, you've almost certainly got some kind of physical problem. Men who lose potency because of emotional upset, poor couple sex technique, or the like almost always have some erections. Either they get an erection during sex play and lose it before intercourse, or they get 'bladder' erections, or they have wet dreams. Any erection at all proves that the mechanism still works and virtually eliminates physical causes. But a fellow who has no erections for a considerable period almost always suffers from a sex organ disorder, a metabolic disease, or some type of drug or medicine effect. Let's check the sex organ problems first: Do you have any burning or stinging when you pass your water?"

"No."

"Any difficulty starting the stream, or any dribbling when you finish?"

"No."

"How about pain or discomfort in the low back or down between your buttocks? Any difficulty there?"

"No, but what would these things mean if I had?"

"Those are the kinds of troubles you get with prostate infection, which also causes impotence at times. I'll feel your prostate gland in a few minutes—I can reach it by putting a finger into the rectum—but if that was your trouble you would probably have some urinary complaints or low back pain. What about drugs and medicines? Are you taking anything for blood pressure or any tranquilizers?"

"No."

"Any stimulants like amphetamine or Dexedrine or Benzedrine? For weight control or pep-up action?"

"No, nothing at all. I haven't taken a pill in months."

"What about sedatives and alcohol? How much do you drink per day?"

"Oh, nothing that regular. I drink maybe three or four beers over the weekend."

"And no sleeping pills?"

"Never."

"Well, we'll just have to take a good hard look at you and see what we can find."

And look we did, at his entire health history and physical state, including urine studies, blood studies, and so forth. The cause of Bob's difficulties finally proved to be in his body's use of sugars. After a high-sugar meal, his blood sugar went abnormally high and stayed there longer than it should. Bob was not a diabetic, and had no other complaints except in the sexual sphere. A special diet low in sugars and starches quickly restored his potency, though, and may have warded off actual diabetes (which often develops within a few years with this kind of sugar curve).

The relationship of potency to the body's use of sugars is a very interesting one. Almost half of the male diabetics below age fifty have potency problems. Some of them recover their full sexual capacity with control of the diabetes, while others do not. So-called pre-diabetics like Bob Metcalf often have trouble, too, which makes detailed blood sugar studies worthwhile in anyone who becomes completely impotent even if there is no sign of a full-fledged diabetic state. I have also had several patients with potency problems related to poor nutrition, apparently due to disordered use of sugars.

Gary Teller almost starved to death during the war. He was a missionary worker who was interned by the Japanese. Instead of fighting for his share of the scanty rations, he gave away half of his food to people who were ill or aged.

When Gary Teller got home, he weighed 89 pounds. Years later, when he first came to me, he weighed 156 pounds and regarded himself as completely over his ordeal. He never had an erection, however, either in the morning, from self-play, in dreams, or in sex. He also needed nine or ten hours of sleep each night to sustain his energy, though he led a very quiet and physically sheltered life.

When a person almost starves, his body shifts from its normal way of using sugars and starches to alternate methods. These alternates greatly increase his need for certain of the B vitamins. Even years afterward—often for the rest of his life—the victim needs many times the normal Vitamin B supply. For this reason, I advised Gary Teller to take four therapeutic strength vitamin capsules a day: many times the normal daily requirement. After a few weeks, he felt much more energetic and required less sleep. And he also began to experience erections. After about three months his potency was fully restored.

Gary Teller was the first patient I ever treated with high doses of vitamin B Complex for metabolic impotence and that was almost an accident: His lack of energy rather than his potency problem led to the original prescription. But he had such good results that I've tried the same program with many other "disordered sugar use" patients, including several with diabetes and several others with abnormal sugar curves like Bob Metcalf's (if they didn't respond to diet alone). Over half of these patients, including one diabetic who had tried everything up to and including thorough regulation at the Mayo Clinic, have regained full potency.

In some cases, nutritional effects are more immediate. Chang Lo had not had an erection for six months, either for intercourse, in the morning, or while asleep. This was the second such interval in his life; he had had a three-month period of impotence two years before.

As a twenty-four-year-old foreign graduate student, Chang had suffered real penury. Currency restrictions sharply limited the money his family could send him, and his student visa did not allow him to work. Each of the periods of impotence occurred when he was cooking for himself, eating irregularly and without regard for variety or nutritional balance. The first episode had cleared up when he moved into a college dormitory which served three meals a day (although he hadn't realized the connection at the time). A similar arrangement plus vitamin capsules cleared up the second episode within three weeks.

You can eat enough to stave off hunger without meeting all your body's food needs. Chang Lo wasn't starving, he just wasn't getting the right variety of foods. I'm sure that a great many people who suffer lags in potency have the same problem, especially as middle age cuts down their activity, their fuel requirements, and their appetites. If you have difficulty getting an erection, give your diet a good hard look. You should be eating something from each of the following groups at virtually every meal:

Meat, fish and eggs.

Milk or milk products.

Bread, cereal or other food derived from grain.

Vegetables, green and yellow.

Fruits, including some citrus.

Vitamin capsules help to fill some nutritional gaps, of course. But they don't always fill the whole bill, and a rounded diet often helps restore sexual capability when vitamins alone fail.

To some extent, the potency problems experienced by heavy drinkers may be on a nutritional basis. Alcohol provides enough body fuel to make regular drinkers cut down on their food intake. Since they tend to keep eating full servings of their favorite dishes, the less favored varieties drop out of the picture. Many drinkers who are not real alcoholics still don't get the meat-milk-vegetable-fruit-grain mixture which provides ideal vitamin and mineral content. When age cuts down activity and slows body processes, decreased appetite makes the problem much worse. There is also a specific toxic element in some cases which vitamins alone cannot correct.

Martin Carson, aged forty-nine, had not had an erection for three months, either in sex play, sleep, or self-stimulation. Martin had never had any trouble because of his drinking; he had been on the same job for fourteen years without any lost weekends, had never been arrested for drunkenness or drunken driving, and had no domestic troubles caused by alcohol. But he was a regular social drinker in the three-to-four-drinks-a-day range.

At my suggestion, Martin gave the "water wagon" a try. After six weeks without liquor, he reported restored erections and normal sex life. "But isn't there any other way?" he asked. I put him on high doses of vitamins, and suggested that he creep up on the drinking to see how much he could stand. On one cocktail a day, plus vitamins, Martin remained fully potent. But with or without vitamins, two drinks a day interfered with full erection, and anything more killed off sex completely.

Different people tolerate different amounts of alcohol. Some seem able to drink quite heavily without affecting their sexual powers, while others, even if they can hold their liquor well in other ways, have trouble with full erection after very few drinks. If you generally take one or more cocktails or highballs every day, though, faulty erections might someday result. If so, it usually takes at least six weeks without alcohol to determine whether abstinence will solve your problem.

Like alcohol, medicines which affect your mood or your body reactions to emotion also can upset your sexual functions. Let's look at three interesting examples.

Peter Armstrong had not had sex for two weeks because of back trouble, and both he and his wife were rather eager for it. But he couldn't manage an erection no matter how he tried. Peter became very upset and visited my office the next day. It turned out that his trouble came from the pills he was taking to relax the muscles in his back. These are exactly the same medicine as tranquilizer pills, and sometimes tone down your response to sexual excitement even more than to other emotion-inducing situations.

Jake Ramberg thought his problem was old age. He was fifty-four when his potency left him, and he more or less shrugged his shoulders and forgot about it. A couple of years later he moved to this area and wound up in my office. Jake's sexual difficulties had actually started a few weeks after his doctor put him on blood-pressure pills. He got an erection fairly readily after skipping his medicine for a week. But without medication his blood pressure went high enough to pose some danger, and so simply omitting the pills for a few days whenever he felt that he was due for sex—which is the approach some milder blood pressure cases use—wasn't the answer. After trying several different preparations, we finally found a pill that controlled Jake's pressure without interfering with his sex life, and suddenly he was "young" again.

Henry Nelson had an unusual complaint. He could get an erection as easily as ever, but only the most prolonged and intense sexual stimulations would bring him to a climax. Long before he reached orgasm, his wife was exhausted, he was exhausted, and the whole thing had ceased to be fun. This difficulty had occurred for a brief period about a year previously and had then disappeared. It recurred six weeks before he came to my office. At first, Henry denied taking any pills or medicines. Then he thought a minute and asked: "Could diet have anything to do with it? Both times I've been trying to lose weight when I started having this trouble."

Actually, diet didn't cause his difficulty, but diet pills did. Henry was taking Dexedrine as an appetite killer without even thinking of it as "medicine." A switch to a different preparation solved his problem. Afterward, several test doses proved conclusively that this medication caused the trouble for Henry Nelson.

Note that I specify "for Henry Nelson," because not everyone gets the same effect. With Henry's case in mind, I have asked men with too-fast ejaculation to try various doses of Dexedrine, but none have been particularly helped. Apparently medicine-related deferral of male orgasm is a response which only particularly sensitive individuals get. But it happens often enough that you should be aware of it, in case you ever suffer a similar effect. Pills sold for appetite control, for mood uplift, and as stimulants for dispelling sleepiness often contain Dexedrine or chemical cousins with similar effects. Some cold capsules can have this action, too. Some of these preparations are supplied in slow release capsules whose effects may be sustained for several days. Any man who has difficulty achieving orgasm in intercourse after taking any such capsules or tablets should discontinue the medication for a week. That usually solves the problem.

When you look for something, you usually find it the last place you look. The reason is obvious: Once you've found it, you don't look anymore.

In the same way, couples who have sex troubles almost never blame their medicines. Once the people involved find the cause of their trouble, they switch to different preparations or skip a few doses as necessary, and the medicine-related sex troubles disappear. But just because you never hear about such difficulties doesn't mean that they don't exist. In fact, medicine-related sex troubles afflict a great many couples at some stage of their communion. If you stay alert for them, you'll usually recognize the situation and either rectify it or live with it without getting upset or losing your sexual confidence, which—especially if you've swallowed the "male menopause" tale —might make quite a difference to your continuing sexual activity.

No matter how old you are, if you stop getting erections altogether, run down the medicine-alcohol-diet checklist, get your doctor to check your prostate gland and your blood sugar curve, and you'll probably find a definite cause you can attack.

But what if you get an erection during sex play, but lose it before you make entrance? Or if you get bladder erections frequently, but never get an erection for sex?

"She'll come up all right," Frank Parsons said, "but she won't hold. She goes soft before I get started."

"You mean you get an erection, but you lose it before you can start intercourse."

"That's right. She won't hold. I haven't given my wife satisfaction for two or three years, and now I can't even get started."

"But you get erections? Good, solid erections in the morning and other times?"

"Sure. She gets good and hard when it doesn't help me, but she won't hold when it would do some good. Of course I'm fifty-two now, and maybe I'm too old. That's what my wife says."

"How old is she?"

"She's fifty."

"And how do you get along?"

"Fine, most ways. She's been a good mother to the children, and she doesn't spend me broke. We squabble once in a while, but never any real fights."

"What about in bed? Does she still appeal to you that way?"

"Always did. And she's always willing, even if she doesn't get much out of it anymore."

"Because of your problem?"

"I guess so. She used to come most of the time, but since I get soft right away she just lies there and tries not to get excited."

"Which isn't too exciting for you either, I imagine."

"Well, no. But what can I expect when I never deliver the goods? She's nice to me, lets me do whatever I want. Lots of fellows would be real glad to settle for that."

"Sure. But let's get back to the very start of your problem, say three years, when you were going good. Tell me about the way you made love then."

"What's there to tell? We did it just like always, with me on top."

"What about play beforehand? You kissed a few times, I suppose."

"Yes, and I always fooled around with her breasts a little, and used my finger till she was ready. Then we got started, and that was that."

"So you always used just about the same approach, the same preliminaries, the same position. Did she ever add any special caresses or extra movement or anything?"

"Caresses? No, nothing like that. She used to move if she was starting to come, that's about all. Otherwise it was all up to me."

"She never put her hand on your penis or kissed it?"

"Lord no! She wouldn't do a thing like that. Maybe once in a while she'd give me a little pat some special way before we ever got started, to let me know that it was going to be one of those nights. But she never put her hand on my privates or anything like that."

The Parsons' sex life was totally routine and unstimulating. No wonder excitement waned on a few occasions, when Frank had done the same things the same way without any extra stimulation at all! And after he had failed a few times, it's no wonder that guilt about one-sided sex, anxiety about whether his erection would hold, and concern about whether old age was catching up created enough emotional turmoil to make sex more and more difficult.

Thousands of "Frank Parsons" slip into sexual limbo each year. Yet a few minutes of couple instruction, if given before failures and recriminations create vast emotional turmoil, would keep most of them sexually active for many years.

"You let Frank do anything he wants," I said to Mrs. Parsons after we had become acquainted. "But don't you ever have an impulse to do something more? Rub yourself against him, or pat him on the fanny or grab his organ?"

"Maybe," she said. "But we don't go for that kind of thing."

"What do you mean?" I asked.

She shrugged squeamishly. "You know, anything out of the way sexually."

"Out of the way?"

"Different, you know. Like anything that might be bad or queer. Queers do it that way, don't they? By playing with each other or putting their mouths on it. I don't know just what they do, but boys who like to be played with aren't quite right."

"That's true if they want to be played all the way past a climax, so that the play *replaces* intercourse instead of *leading up* to it. But there's nothing wrong with play before intercourse, either to get ready or simply for the extra enjoyment it can give."

"We've never done anything like that."

"What about the other way? Frank plays with you beforehand, doesn't he?"

"Sure. I would never get anything out of it without a little head start. And even if I'm not getting very much out of it, he has to help me a little bit or else it hurts."

"That's right. At first, *you* had to have help to get excited and ready. Now *he* has to have help for the same reasons. There really isn't any difference as to right or wrong. The only difference is that he can play you past a climax without doing harm, because you'll be ready again almost right away. You have to be careful not to push him past a climax, but that won't be hard."

At this point, we went over the kind of genital caress a woman can use to stimulate her husband. Both the Parsonses seemed a bit hesitant at first, but they finally agreed to give active caress a full trial.

"It's just as important to realize what *isn't* causing your trouble as to understand what *is*," I said after the various techniques were clear. "Frank's age has nothing to do with it, and neither has yours. Maybe you were a little more attractive sexually when you were twenty than you are today, but the fact that Frank has had sexual fun with you time after time has linked in his mind the sight and smell and feel of you quite strongly with sex. This tie-in has made you more and more stimulating to him sexually, and helps make up for anything you've lost. He needs extra caressing to get ready for sex now, just as you've needed it all along, but it's not because you've lost your basic sex appeal. It's just because you've both let your couple sex technique get into a rut, and a rut that doesn't really suit your present time of life. A little variety, sex techniques that are right for a mature couple, and a chance to build confidence again ought to set you right in a hurry."

Which actually happened. Frank called me after a month to say that he was having good solid erections that lasted all the way through, and that sex with adequate preparation had proved more satisfying than anything they had enjoyed in the past.

Even an expert cannot always tell which comes first, impotence or emotional upset. Like the chicken and the egg, each leads to the other. In a great many cases, though, an attack on a person's general discouragement and depression works out better than remedies aimed at impotence alone.

Steve G. had lost interest in sex. In fact, he had lost interest in almost everything. Shortly after his fiftieth birthday, he began to feel that life was futile, that he would never accomplish anything any more, and that he had been guilty of many past crimes and sins. He had lost his appetite and had been resting poorly, waking early in the morning and being unable to go back to sleep. Constipation plagued him. He sometimes felt so blue that he would weep, especially when he was alone.

Although impotence was his most prominent complaint, Steve's physical and mental processes were all depressed. Without treatment, he may well have gone on into deeper depression and perhaps attempted suicide. Antidepressant medications restored his functioning in all spheres.

A fairly severe depression like Steve's has its advantages. He got treatment right away and recovered completely. A great many men get depressed just enough to lose interest in sex, figure they're too old, and never regain enough confidence to resume marital relations. Certainly, loss of sexual capacity or interest accompanied by weight loss, constipation, and a depressed or agitated mood deserves evaluation by a doctor. Quite often simple treatment can restore your capacity to live a full life in every way and thereby avoid vicious-circle sexual difficulties which might otherwise persist for the rest of your life, years after the depression itself is gone.

Peter R. married when he was forty-two. Although he had managed intercourse without difficulty on several occasions before, his wedding night proved a complete fiasco. During the next three months he never achieved an erection in bed. Morning erections continued, proving his physical power, but sex play never once aroused him.

Peter had felt trapped in an uncomfortable relationship with his mother for many years. When she died two years before his marriage, he felt simultaneously relieved and lost. After a lifetime of confused love-hatred for the only woman in his life, he was far from ready to enter the intimacy of a truly loving marriage, and his initial failure only made things worse. He went the whole psychoanalytic course with a highly qualified specialist, but he never achieved real success.

In cases like his, psychiatric treatment helps in a special way: Only a few people really get well and learn to love, but many of the rest learn to live with other people in a comfortable if not wholly satisfying way. Total success is the exception rather than the rule, after one's life patterns are thoroughly set in a way that makes women difficult to love.

The male menopause is a vicious myth.

If you believe that statement, you will at least avoid the vicious circle of *temporary difficulty* leading to *partial impotence* leading to *anxiety, loss of confidence,* and more *impotence.* You will at least look for causes whenever your powers desert you, and perhaps will get medical help when you can't find the causes yourself. Sex in the sixties and seventies, like life itself in the eighties or nineties, might not seem too worthwhile to people of younger years. It seems a lot more important when you get there, though. Why should you miss out on decades of deep satisfaction and couple joy because of a foolish rumor our society has been too prim to set at rest? Perhaps someday you will be too tired or too weak or too sick for sex, but you will never be just plain too old. At least you will never be too old if you convince yourself *right now* that your powers can and should last as long as your health.

7. Sex and the Pill

"I just don't want my husband anywhere near me," Judy Marlowe said. "Not that I don't love him. That's what I can't understand. I want to make him happy, but whenever he puts his hands on me it makes me shudder."

"How long has it been like that?" I asked.

"Almost a year. We were getting along fine until I got pregnant. Then everything sort of turned off."

"Nothing went wrong with the pregnancy?"

"No. It was perfectly normal. I had stitches, of course, and stayed sore for a while. But Harold didn't hurt me or anything. I don't see how that could have anything to do with it."

"How about your sex urge during pregnancy? Some women find they have perfectly normal desire, and others have little or no interest in sex at such times."

"I guess I'm one of the no-interest girls. We had intercourse a few times, but I was never really in the mood."

"What about before you were pregnant? Did you respond more at some times in the month than at others?"

"Yes. Just after my period was finished, sex was always fine. But just before my period I didn't want anything to do with it."

"Sounds as if hormones might have something to do with your problem. The hormones in your blood during the last few days before menstruation ordinarily are almost the same as those during a pregnancy. Your system is loaded with progesterone both times, and that's when you've felt the least interest."

"But what's that got to do with now? I'm not pregnant, and I don't seem to have the urge any time, before periods, after periods, or in between."

"Maybe you're taking hormones without realizing it—birth control pills, for instance."

"I'm on the pill, all right."

"All one color or two different-colored pills?"

"All one color. But I thought the pill was more likely to help my responses than to hurt them."

"That's true in some cases, because of the relief it gives from pregnancy fears. But the pill affects you in more ways than one, and sometimes one bad effect can overbalance several good ones. Pregnancy fears can end an urge, but if progesterone keeps you from getting any urge in the first place, relief of pregnancy fears can't do a bit of good."

"Can one pill a day do all that? I mean it doesn't seem a big enough deal to affect the way you think and feel all through the day and night."

"Your normal body hormones control cells all over your tissues. One tiny dose of hormone gives commands to millions of your body cells, and has tremendous effects. A dose of hormone can be like an enemy spy in command of your body: It gives the 'wrong' orders to the whole body."

"Then one tiny progesterone pill a day could kill my sex urge completely?"

"Yes, if you happen to react that way. Look what the same amount of hormone every day does to an adolescent: not only turns her from a flat-chested stringy-legged youngster to a curvaceously mature woman but also makes boys crucial to her feeling of worth and intimate caress vital to her peace of mind. In a sense, hormones have to give you a sex urge before psychology has anything to do with it. And if you react badly to progesterone, hormones can take away your sex urge no matter what the emotional framework might be."

"Then it's back to the diaphragm for me?"

"No, the diaphragm is pretty well out as far as I'm concerned. Either Delfen or Emko foam—I'll write down those names for you, and you can get them at any drugstore without a prescription—give better protection with less folderol."

"How do I use them?"

"There's an applicator with the foam dispenser—a smooth plastic tube with a plunger in it. You fill the applicator with foam, insert it into the vagina just as if it was a tampon, then push the plunger to deposit foam well inside. It's better to use two applicatorsful when you're using foam as your only means of birth control. Don't worry too much about timing, though. The directions say you should apply foam within an hour before intercourse, but I would just put it in at bedtime and let nature take its course. Most couples find that it's better to waste a little material getting ready too often than to wait until you're sure intercourse is in the offing. Otherwise your husband often feels as if you've taken over control of the sex pace. Foam is instant protection, though. If an urge catches you unprepared, you're ready as soon as you finish the application. Ordinarily you'll be protected for four hours or more but after you have intercourse once, the secretions will thin the foam enough that you'll need another dose before repeating that same night."

"How good is the protection? I didn't think any of the methods were one hundred percent except the pill."

"Foam failures average one in each twenty years, which makes it about twice as effective as a rubber or a diaphragm. Of course, that 'one in twenty years' could happen in the first ten minutes, but it really isn't very likely. Suppose you need six months to tell whether the pill is your whole trouble. The odds are forty to one against a pregnancy in that time."

"*Will* I need six months to tell?"

"Probably not. Most couples get back to normal in two or three months if the pill is the only cause of their trouble. There are enough exceptions, though, that you shouldn't give up in less than six months at the very least —one prominent group of sex doctors won't attempt any other approach to female sex aversion until the patient has been off the pill eighteen months or more."

"But why foam instead of a diaphragm?"

"Mainly because it interferes less with couple satisfaction. A diaphragm doesn't bother you much the first few months of marriage when most of your sexual sensitivity is in the clitoris (which the diaphragm doesn't cover). But after a few months many areas which the diaphragm does cover become sexually attuned. From then on, intercourse with a diaphragm on is like taking a shower in a raincoat as far as the woman is concerned. If you're already having trouble achieving orgasms, a diaphragm just makes matters worse."

"All right. So I use foam for a while to see whether the pill has anything to do with my lack of response. If it does, what happens next? Can I ever get on the pill again?"

"Not on the same kind of pill. Fortunately, there's another type which works on an entirely different principle, and which usually won't give you the same trouble."

"Then how did you know which kind I'm taking?"

"Because yours are all one color. If you take the same color pill all the way through your cycle, it has to be the pregnancy-simulating variety.* The pills that work by confusing the cycle come in two different colors. You take one color for most of the menstrual cycle and the other color for the days just preceding menstruation."

"So how are they different?"

"Pregnancy-simulating pills take advantage of the fact that your ovaries do not release more egg cells once one egg has been fertilized and rooted in the womb. Multiple births are no exceptions: They are from eggs released before any of them gets implanted. Once a pregnancy is off to a good start, the implanted fetus puts hormones into the mother's bloodstream which signal her system to turn off egg cell production; otherwise, you might wind up with two babies in the uterus a month or two apart in age, and it would be impossible for the pregnancy to end right for both of them. By taking hormones of the kind that circulate in your bloodstream during pregnancy, you trigger the turn-off mechanism, your ovaries stop releasing egg cells, and you don't get pregnant. But you may have

---

* However, not all pregnancy-simulating pills are one color. At least one manufacturer includes some inert pills of a different color so that the patient can take a pill every day of the month and thereby keep in the habit.

many side effects, ranging from morning sickness to loss of sex urge. Some of the newer forms of pregnancy-simulating pill cut these side effects way down by decreased hormone dosage, since with experience drug manufacturers have been able to find just how small a dose they can put in a pill without losing effectiveness—but they haven't eliminated side effects altogether. If progesterone knocks out your sex urge, pregnancy-simulating pills might have this effect."

"What about the other pills?"

"They work by confusing the control system for your menstrual cycle instead of by simulating pregnancy.

"Instead of fooling your body into thinking you're pregnant, they just fool your pituitary gland into thinking your ovaries have already released an egg cell. Then your pituitary gland puts the brakes on as far as the ovaries are concerned, and shifts your system from its egg-preparing to its preparation for pregnancy phase. In your normal cycle, the pituitary gets hormone signals from the ovaries and then signals the ovaries what to do. The cycle-confusing pills, with their artificial ovarian hormones, simply fool the pituitary into never giving the egg-release signal. This approach works just about as well as the pregnancy-simulating one, but the hormones involved are much closer to the kind you usually have in your body."

"You mean they don't have progesterone in them?"

"They do, but only in the pills you take a few days out of the month—just about the same number of days your ovaries usually make progesterone anyway. The other days you take estrogens—hormones which generally affect your sex urge favorably if they affect it at all."

"Then why can't I go straight onto this kind of pill?"

"You can, if you find the barest possibility of a pregnancy or the bother of getting ready with foam really disturbing. I can prescribe a sequential birth control tablet* for you, and you can switch at the time of your next period. But it would be better for you to get away from all artificial hormones for a while, to be absolutely sure progesterone is the whole problem. Then if you do have any further difficulties we can attack them with confidence that the pill has nothing to do with them."

"In other words, with the foam I can start right away instead of waiting till my next period. I'll probably know where I stand in a month or so, and if the pill proves to be the whole answer I can try a different kind of pill with reasonable chance that I won't get my trouble back?"

"That's right. And if getting off the pill doesn't relieve the situation I'll see you again in three months and we'll start on some different approaches."

Judy Marlowe phoned about six weeks later to ask for the sequential pill prescription. Her sexual nature had returned to normal in about three weeks. Cycle-confusing hormones proved to have no adverse effects on her sex life, and she has continued to use them for about two years.

If the pill dampens your sex urge, you may not be able to identify the source of the difficulty as easily as you might expect. Unless you have already formed a good sexual adjustment and know what to expect of yourself and your mate, you may simply accept the way things are without ever realizing that they could be different. You may have pill-related trouble, but blame the problem on changed circumstances like a new baby in the house or a different job—events which often occasion change in birth control technique and thus coincide with pill-induced problems. Or the problem may come on slowly. I have had a number of patients whose sex urge remained active or even in-

* Norquen, Oracon, and Ortho-novum SQ are the best-known brands, all available on prescription only.

creased for the first few months on the pills, who then lost sexual interest very gradually over a period of six to eighteen months. Incidentally, these women usually had to use foam or sequential pills for several months before restoring sex urge—much longer than girls whose trouble started immediately after they went on the pill.

The practical points can be stated quite briefly:

1. If your sex urge lags the week before menstruation and almost disappears during pregnancy, don't use the pregnancy-simulating pills. The sequential variety, with one color taken fifteen days or so, a different color taken five days or so, and a period with no pills at all thereafter are much less likely to upset your sexual nature.

2. If you are taking birth control pills and have an aversion to sex play or intercourse, switch to foam or some other means of birth control. Ordinarily you will note a change in your nature within a few weeks, but remember that you can't be absolutely sure that the pill has no bad effects on you for six months to a year, especially if your trouble came on slowly.

3. Don't neglect such a trial just because there's something else to blame your trouble on, such as a new baby or changed living circumstances, or because the pill seemed to add to your sex urge at first.

Nobody really knows just how frequently women develop sexual aversion because of the pill. About one woman in five notes a decrease in sex urge just before menstruation, which means that some adverse reaction to progesterone is rather common. Experts in the field only see the women who have troubles, though, and have no idea how many others take the same pills without any difficulty at all.

Gynecologists generally encounter fewer cases like Judy Marlowe's than they do of the opposite problem. Here's a report of what they have found to be the commonest kind of pill-related couple sex difficulty:

"I don't know what's gone wrong," Mabel Smith said. "Jerry just doesn't make many advances any more."

"I would if she gave me a chance," Jerry said. "She's after me all the time—never gives me a chance to start anything—always nagging at me and talking as if I've lost my manhood. But there's nothing wrong with my manhood except I'm tired of being nagged about it, and how can I get interested if she won't give me a chance?"

"Let's get a little firmer picture of your problem. You can have an erection easily enough and carry through to a climax without losing it?"

"Sure. I've never had any trouble coming through for her yet, once she lets me get in the mood."

"And how often do you get in the mood? How many times have you had intercourse this month, for instance?"

"Let's see, once this week, and she was menstruating the week before. Twice the week before that, and—I can't remember."

"Just once the week before, and not at all the week before that," Mabel said. "And he used to be after me three or four times a week."

"After you?" I asked. "You mean he made advances or you had relations that often?"

"Made advances, I guess. I wasn't always in the mood."

"That's the truth!" Jerry exclaimed. "As long as we were using the diaphragm, she'd turn me down three times out of four. But now she's after me 'most all the time."

As you can tell from lightning mathematics, the Smiths had intercourse almost exactly as often when Mabel was "turning him down" as when she was "after him all the time." After the pill eased her pregnancy fears and exposed previously diaphragm-covered nerve centers, though, her attitude toward sex took an about-face. Her reluctance disappeared and she began to seek sex actively, making a substantial change in couple dynamics.

Why should that upset her husband? Because Jerry was the sort of person who found anything *different* automatically *suspicious*. Since men usually make the first sexual advances, there seemed to be something wrong with the new approach. Jerry never stopped to analyze what was wrong about it or why it bothered him, but he reacted badly to his wife's grabbing of the couple sexual reins—so badly that he hardly even realized that he had been hoping for something very similar only a few months before.

"It sounds to me as if the two of you have very similar sexual needs," I said after we had talked the matter over a bit. "When Mabel was reluctant you pressed her for intercourse quite often. Now the tables are turned and she's pressing you for it often. But what counts is not how often you *ask*, but how often you *get* it, and that stays about the same whichever of you is in the driver's seat."

"So what does that prove?" Jerry asked belligerently.

"I don't know whether it proves anything, but it suggests that there should be a way for the two of you to get along. Back when you were eager all the time and Mabel was ready only once a week, I'm sure that she was worried about what would happen if she let you have your way. She could see your marriage turning into a sex orgy if you really wanted sex as often as you asked for it."

"That's right," Mabel interrupted.

"But it's like when somebody knocks on your door," I went on. "If you open right away he only knocks once, but if you don't open he knocks three or four times. Most wives who find their husband after them for sex all the time are surprised at how little their sex pace changes when they give in every time. And that's exactly what's happened here: Your couple pace is hardly different with *you* digging in your heels than it was when *she* was hanging back. So the problem isn't really how often you have intercourse, is it?"

"Maybe not," Jerry said. "But she just never gives me a chance."

"You mean she never lets you start things off, be the aggressor, act out the male role?"

"That's right."

I paused for a moment, hoping one of them would pick up the "male role" issue. But neither did.

"The male role," I repeated. "I guess most people think that starting things is the male's role."

I paused again, and this time Mabel took the bait.

"Then what does that make me?" she asked. "If I want sex and go after it, does that make me some kind of freak or something?"

"That's one question," I said. "And another is what does it make Jerry? If sexual aggression really is the male role—and I'm not saying it is—what does that make of the man who only acquiesces?"

I turned expectantly to Jerry and awaited an answer.

"I guess it makes him some kind of a freak or something," he said. "But I don't feel like I'm a freak, and I don't feel there's anything wrong with Mabel either. It's just that she never gives me a chance."

"And that upsets you."

"Yes. I want a chance to start things off the way a fellow should. . . . Say, I'm beginning to see what you mean. Is it that I get all upset not because I'm being pushed out of my depth but because I think letting Mabel start things all the time makes me less of a man?"

"That's one way to put it. But there's a funny thing

about the human mind. The kind of conflict that really upsets you isn't one with someone else; it's an argument inside yourself. The thing that disturbs you about Mabel's advances isn't what they themselves do to you; it's what your inner response to them does to *you*. You *like* having Mabel make some of the advances, and there's really nothing in the world wrong with your liking it. But as long as you think this way of getting started may be odd-ball, a big part of your mind doesn't like having you like it. And that's what upsets you: the fact that you actually like being made love to by Mabel, mixed with the fact that you sort of suspect that liking the 'other role' makes a freak of you."

"And really it doesn't?"

"Not at all. You're still trying to please *each other* sexually, and the way you go about it still involves *masculine, assertive action*. The fact that you've pleased your wife so much that she wants and needs you is certainly no reflection on your masculinity. Maybe she ought to play her cards a little differently—we'll talk about that in a minute—but there's nothing abnormal or weird about a woman making advances, and nothing whatever wrong with a man who enjoys being made love to by an active partner once in a while."

"God knows I didn't want to change anything," Mabel said. "I *like* to have Jerry take the lead in lovemaking. But if I want it more often than he does what can I do?"

"You can try to stir Jerry's interest with earlier and more subtle methods. I suppose you've already tried the negligee-and-perfume instead of cold-cream-and-hair-curlers approach. A lot of women who complain that their husbands aren't interested can do a great deal to make themselves more attractive in the evening and at bedtime, and I never heard a husband complain about money spent on sleek nightgowns."

Mabel looked a bit chagrined.

"I guess we all get in some bad habits," she said, and I could tell that the hair curlers had hit home.

"There's nothing wrong with letting Jerry know you're interested," I went on. "The trick is to do so in ways that let him still feel like the boss of your couple sex life. Any form of eye appeal, conversation, suggestive caresses, or gentle kisses will probably excite his interest without making him feel that you've taken over. More direct measures work fine once he's shown signs of beginning excitement, but not beforehand."

"I don't quite understand," Mabel said.

"Suppose he's driving you home from a party and you put your hand on his thigh. That probably excites him, but doesn't commit him to anything. Now when you get into the house he gives you a kiss and lets his hand stray onto your breast. Then you reach for his zipper—by then he doesn't mind a bit. But suppose you reached for his zipper as soon as you got in the house. Then he'd probably feel as if you were taking over the reins and threatening his male role. Any caress that ordinarily occurs after you both know you're headed for intercourse should be saved until after Jerry has made some advances of his own, partly so you're sure he's interested and partly so that he can feel in control."

"I suppose it would help if I told her," Jerry said. "I've always been afraid to say anything that might sound critical, though."

"Which is pretty smart. A lot of experts talk about improved communications on matters of sex without warning you that it can go too far. You should let each other know what pleases you and what displeases you, but only as long as you can do it *without insulting the woman's charm or the man's masculinity.* If there's a chance of harming the relationship, it's better to forget the criticism no matter how constructive it seems. There are some forms of expression that can't do anything but good—the natural 'oohs' and 'ahs' you feel impelled toward by sexual delight, any honest compliments. But I don't think you should work too hard telling her what you think she's doing wrong, unless you can do it in a very diplomatic way indeed."

"Then what *can* I do to help? You said there were things for both of us to do."

"When Mabel says she wants more sex, she means that she wants more attention, more fondling, more caress. Maybe she wants more orgasms, too, but that's almost secondary. The main thing she wants is physical contact in the framework of love. Do you think you can give her more of that without any real strain? That you can spend a little more time on preliminaries, or hold her in your arms sometimes without necessarily going on to full-fledged sex? That you could play her past a climax during the preliminaries and still get her an orgasm in intercourse a few minutes later?"

Jerry nodded, and after a few minutes of further discussion the Smiths left my office. They reported two weeks later that everything was fine.

The male fear of homosexuality combined with ignorance about what constitutes maleness—what sexual behavior, likes and dislikes, really are properly male—sets the stage for reactions like Jerry Smith's. Actually, no incident which ends in a heterosexual climax has any homosexual factor in it. A man can enjoy anything his wife does to him without guilt so long as both have intercourse as their ultimate goal. Getting that fact straight might not solve all the sex pace problems produced by pill-inspired release from pregnancy fears, but it certainly lets you work together to attack any disharmonies which remain.

8. Sex and the Menopause

Everybody knows that worry about whether a woman might get pregnant can curtail her sexual response. For this reason, you might presume that the end of fertility, either through natural menopause or surgical procedure, would *help* not *hurt* a woman's sex life. It can, but exactly the opposite result often occurs.

"They told me that having my uterus out wouldn't affect my sex life," Lilian Benson said. "But it has. Ever since my hysterectomy, I just can't get fired up. Nothing Pete does seems to get through to me."

"How long has it been since the operation?" I asked.

"About a year."

"What was wrong?"

"Nothing malignant. Fibroid tumors."

"And your doctor took out the whole uterus without leaving a stub of cervix behind."

"Right. He specifically said I wouldn't have to worry about Pap tests or anything from now on. But he left me my ovaries, and told me I wouldn't be affected any way at all except that I wouldn't have monthly periods and I can't get pregnant."

"All right. Let's check on the physical situation first, then we'll discuss your problem further."

Lilian had healed perfectly. Her entire uterus had been removed, including the cervix, which is the portion that normally juts into the vagina. The cervix is about one inch wide, so its removal always causes a temporary sore spot high up on the front of the vagina and shortens that organ a bit. In Lilian's case, there was no remaining tenderness, but she did report occasional twinges of discomfort on deep penetration during intercourse.

"I guess Pete's pretty large that way," she said. "He always did have to be a little careful not to hit bottom. As long as I'm fully relaxed we don't have any trouble, but once or twice he's hit me wrong and it's been really bad."

"Maybe we ought to talk about this 'hitting bottom' business," I said. "If you go by the anatomy charts, you'd think that intercourse would tear a woman apart. They always list the vagina as four inches long, with the vestibule adding only another inch or less. When you figure that a large male organ may be nine inches or so, it sounds out of proportion. Even if you compare the size of your husband's organ with the biggest tampon inserter you can use, you wonder how you can ever manage intercourse. But in actual fact, the vagina elongates considerably when you become sexually excited. Penises enlarge somewhat too, but the ones which are large when limp tend to enlarge much less than the smaller ones so that none of them gets beyond the capacity of a thoroughly relaxed vagina."

"But everybody talks about hitting bottom sometimes."

"Yes, lots of women get a spasm of pain occasionally at the height of a deep sexual thrust. But in most cases what actually happens is that the penis has either caught on the front rim of the cervix or has pinched some tender structure like an ovary between the vagina and the pubic bone. These twinges of pain almost always happen in sexual positions which direct the male thrust forward—when the wife's heels are on her husband's shoulders, for example, or when her thighs are in the hollow of her husband's flanks. In these positions, the penis actually enters at an angle from the vagina's back rim toward its front surface. The penis doesn't penetrate as far this way as it does when it is lined up directly with the vagina in more ordinary posture, but it does thrust strongly along the front wall of the vagina where it can catch against the cervix or pinch the ovaries."

"So you think my discomfort doesn't come from Pete going in too far, but just in the wrong direction."

"Probably. If your problem before surgery was actually a pinched ovary, the ovary is still there and in the course of the operation was probably sewed up snug near the outer surface of the vagina. So the answer for you would be the same as for any woman with painful twinges during sex: an emphasis on making your husband enter from straight on or from a slightly front-to-back angle. Here's the way it works."

I put my finger into her vagina, lined up directly with its axis.

"In the ordinary sex position, with your legs spread,

your knees bent and your feet flat on the bed, your husband's thrust lines up directly with your vagina. But even in this position you can wind up with some back-to-front thrust. If you rock your hips forward—try it now, so I can show you what happens—your husband's angle of entry is changed so that the tip of his penis goes along the front wall of your vagina instead of straight in. The same type of friction occurs in the legs-up postures even when you don't move your body at all. As soon as you raise your legs, your hips roll forward and your husband's entry angle shifts in the undesirable way.

"Now look at what happens when you put one leg down straight. Your hips roll back a bit and your husband's angle of entry shifts front-to-back. This directs the thrust of the penis away from any possibly tender structures. It doesn't change depth of penetration much, but it still almost always prevents hitting bottom, usually makes intercourse comfortable somewhat sooner after surgery, and generally proves sort of a panacea for sporadic spasms of pain during intercourse."

"I'm not sure what I'm supposed to do, though. You mean just keep my leg down straight during intercourse?"

"With mild problems like yours, you probably can just avoid the more extreme legs-up postures. But if you feel tense or have other reason to believe you might have trouble, just keep one or both legs down and I think you'll avoid spasms of pain altogether. Your husband can straddle the leg you have down, or both legs if you put them both down, instead of trying to keep his knees between yours. Most couples find that they can shift into these positions more easily after the male has already made sexual entrance than if they start off that way."

"That sounds easy enough. But I still can't get over the idea that the vagina is sometimes too short. Haven't I read about women who were seriously injured?"

"Yes, under circumstances which keep the vagina from relaxing. Severe pain or great emotional upset can make the vagina clamp down like a vise. A couple engaged in sexual intercourse when the bed catches on fire sometimes literally can't get themselves apart, for instance. In rape or other conditions leading to great turmoil the woman's vagina may remain unrelaxed and the penis can actually penetrate its walls. But if you're a willing partner and your husband takes even a little time getting you ready, there's absolutely no danger from sexual intercourse. And the amount of shortening involved in your kind of surgery doesn't affect the issue, either.

"Anxiety about whether you're going to have a spasm of pain can quench your response altogether, especially if you've been led to believe that the spasms you have had in the past show that your husband is just on the edge of causing you serious injury. That's why I'd like to have you try sex in the guaranteed-safe-from-pain-spasms positions for a few weeks before we go any further."

Lilian gave guarded positions a thorough try, and reported that she did feel more relaxed about sex as the weeks passed without a spasm of discomfort. But she still didn't reach a climax, and in view of the fact that her former responsiveness proved a higher potential I suggested further counseling. We had several meetings before a highly significant exchange developed. We were talking about women—what makes a person worthwhile as a woman, what criteria a woman can use to judge her adequacy—when Lilian suddenly exclaimed:

"Oh, what's the use? I'm not a woman. Not a real one, anyway."

Tears filled her eyes. She paused but I waited for her to go on.

"Not since my operation. There's really nothing left of me down there—nothing that counts."

"Your uterus is gone. Everything else is there. You can do anything you ever could, except have children."

"But that's what it's all about, isn't it? That's the whole idea."

"Maybe that's what they taught you in school. But do you really believe it? Do you respect your girl friends according to how large their families are, and write them off when they pass the menopause?"

"No, but I don't respect them for being hot numbers in bed, either. When you come right down to it, this whole woman's world is phony. We get respect for picking the right clothes and keeping up the house instead of choosing the right husband and raising children well."

"In a sense you're right. None of us would be here if women didn't have babies, and we'd be a darn sight worse off if they hadn't tried to rear them right. But there's still a lot more to life than reproduction for any woman, and a lot of other ways for her to earn self-respect."

"All right, there's more to life than just reproduction. But we're not talking about life, are we? We're talking about the real reasons for things—what makes them right and all the rest."

"That's an interesting statement—what makes them right."

"Well, that's what sex is for, isn't it? Having babies."

"And pleasing husbands, and showing love, and building the kind of emotional atmosphere you need in the home both for child-rearing and for a workable marriage."

"I hadn't thought of it like that."

"Why not? Even the Catholic church, which for years taught that sex for any purpose except reproduction was a sin, recognizes these other functions. The latest Papal pronouncements on the subject clearly state that sex in marriage is right and proper for expression of love and building a wholesome atmosphere at home. At this point, I don't know of any major religious or social group which would argue the point. So I can't really believe that having your uterus out affects the rightness or wrongness of married sex in any way, anymore than it affects your ability to please your husband."

One bald pronouncement didn't do the trick, of course. But Lilian mulled over the matter and discussed it further on several visits. Then she dropped out of my sight for a while. But a few months later she sent me a brief note to say that things were fine.

A number of different problems contribute to sexual unresponsiveness after hysterectomy, including fear of injury, mourning for lost feminine parts and for lost reproductive capability, identification of womanhood with reproduction, guilt about sex for other purpose than reproduction, and sometimes guilt about having undergone the operation at least partially for birth control. Fortunately, none of these factors stems from the deeply rooted attitudes and emotional response patterns which require prolonged, systematic psychotherapy. Husband-wife discussion, a few frank questions raised with the gynecologist, and perhaps a rereading of Lilian Benson's case report should generally resolve the issue.

A great many of these same factors enter into the menopausal picture, complicated further by the physical effects of hormonal change. Rapid decrease in ovarian function causes hot flashes, sudden sweats, creeping sensations on the skin, and some subtle changes in body chemistry. Most of the other problems of the menopausal period stem from the time of life itself—as one patient put it, from the fact that "you know that there won't be any more second chances—that your figure will never get better, you'll never be any more attractive, you'll have to dress more and more discreetly and less and less for charm." For some women, this "there's no tomorrow" sensation consummates a feeling of sexual failure, for others it magnifies anxiety or guilt. Since all of these responses impair sexual response, upheavals in the marriage relationship often transcend the apparent personal crisis.

In the reproduction-centered world of a generation ago, this crisis generally occurred when the menopause signaled the end of the fertile period. In our youth-and-sex-centered world of today, the first real evidences of decline in physical attraction light the fuse. The menopause looms more as a further threat than as an actual crisis, and the predominant anxieties most women express relate mainly to post-menopausal dumpiness and lost attraction rather than to infertility. Most people today seem aware of the fact that postmenopausal women keep their full power to respond sexually, and that even if they lose the urgency of their need for sex they still retain easily awakened desire and full capability. They do not fear the menopause; they fear the long, long road that they will travel after loss of attraction sharply restricts their choice. Here are a few brief cases which demonstrate this point.

"We've been going along and going along for twenty-two years," Jean S. said. "Now we've got to get this settled. Maybe we haven't too much time left, but what we have is going to be right."

The issue, of course, was mutual sexual satisfaction, and a one-visit rundown on couple technique seemed helpful.

"I've put up with his flirting and ogling and all the rest," Mabel B. said. "But now it's got to stop."

Why? Because Mabel was losing confidence in her attractions. At some level, she had always felt sure that she could win her husband back from any other woman, or that if she didn't want him back she could win somebody else. But suddenly she didn't feel so sure.

"I've never had a climax, not once in all these years. Maybe it's Henry, maybe it's me, maybe we just don't go about it right. But if it's going to happen, it has to be soon, so we just made up our minds to do something about it."

A good share of all the patients I have seen have been driven to my office (at least partly) by the feeling that time was running out, that attractiveness was on the wane, that things had to be settled now or endured in ever-worsening form. If this notion jolts them out of an unpleasant, repairable rut, perhaps it does some good. But the element of anxiety in it, the feeling of being trapped in a vehicle which is hurtling toward destruction, the no-chance-to-get-or-give-what's-due depression—all of these add emotional turmoil to the problems already bearing down upon them. And in a constant, reasonably strong relationship all of this is for naught.

The attraction that builds up between a couple through years of conditioning—through associating the particular sights and smells and contours of a partner with keen gratification—generally outweighs the erosions of time on outright physical appeal. A couple with a deep and firmly established man-woman relationship in which sex plays a distinct part may find the frequency of intercourse dropping off a bit as the years go by but usually do not lose attraction for each other, and generally find their relationship easier rather than more difficult as the urgencies of sex diminish to clear options. In fact, this harmonious future—maintained attraction, decreased urgency-generated friction, smooth (but not total) shift from physical to companionate enjoyment of each other's presence—is a big argument for the viewpoint that sex should be an expression of man-woman feeling rather than a mutual or a recompensed service. Couples who treat sex as lovemaking endure the pre- and postmenopausal strains much better than those who treat sex as a commodity and marriage as merely a contract through which both parties can get their fill.

"Maybe it seems foolish to you," Maude Simms said. "But can't I have an operation or something to tighten up my vagina again? Ever since I had my children, George just doesn't get the same satisfaction as before, and it's getting to be a real problem."

"How many children have you had?"

"Just four, but they were big ones and they came pretty fast. I didn't get to the delivery room for either of the last two, so things got pretty well stretched and torn."

"And your sex life was perfectly all right before?"

"Maybe not perfect—whose is? But I could always satisfy my husband, and here lately I just can't. Sometimes he'll get started all right and then just lose it right in the middle, because he doesn't get any feeling at all when he's inside."

"Well, let's take a look. I think we should be able to give you some help, and without resorting to surgery if things turn out the way I expect."

Maude's internal organs proved entirely normal. Her vulva showed only a slight separation of the outer lips with the vaginal mucosa barely evident between, not unusual after childbirth. The important point in judging whether surgery will help is how much extra bulging occurs when you cough or strain, which is a point any woman can get some idea of for herself. If you bear down as if you were having a bowel movement, the vagina will become a little more prominent. But if distinct bulges appear at the front and back, pushing the deep-ridged vaginal mucosa well out into the smoothly lined vulva, childbirth stretching has damaged the walls between the vagina and the bladder or rectum. Besides altering sexual frictions, such damage often causes stagnation and infection in the bladder and contributes to constipation. An operation thus can benefit in three ways and becomes almost inevitable in the long run. Sometimes straining will also push the mouth of the uterus down to or through the vulva, again a cause for surgery. Maude had neither of these changes, though. Her vagina was somewhat larger than average, but without the types of relaxation which usually cause further physical disorder.

"I don't want to rule out surgery altogether," I told her. "If everything else fails, you might get some help from an operation. But you can probably take care of your particular situation by strengthening the muscles in the area and by using slightly different sex techniques.

"First of all, I want you to do some exercises. Your vagina is made up almost entirely of muscle. And the surrounding tissues are muscle, too, which can give a great deal of support to the vagina and contribute a great deal to both your husband's pleasure and your own. In fact, some experts believe that good muscle tone in the pelvic floor is the most important physical element in improved feminine responsiveness—that you need good, strong muscles in this area to reach a climax, and that the strength of these muscles actually determines how keen a climax you receive."

"But I can't really make those muscles move, can I?"

"Not unless you train yourself first. The basic setup resembles that of the bladder in some respects. The muscle tissue in the vagina itself, like that in the bladder, is of the involuntary type. It's like the muscle of your intestines, working completely without your conscious control. But the surrounding muscles are more like the sphincters with which you close off your urinary passage and your bowel. They aren't naturally in your conscious control, but you can train yourself to use them. And just as the involuntary muscles of the bladder contract when your brain signals the semivoluntary sphincter muscles, all of the muscle tissue in your female organs can react to exercises or voluntary sexual action."

"You mean I can learn to control the muscles in my vagina?"

"To some extent. You probably can't learn to move any *one* part of your female organ, since all those muscles generally work together in predetermined patterns. But you can deliberately get *all* of the muscles to contract together during strengthening exercises, and you can deliberately get them started working during sexual contact."

"But wouldn't that be an awful distraction? I'm not sure I could respond at all if I was concentrating on doing something fancy with my female organ or the muscles down there."

"Exercises can strengthen the muscles enough to help you even if you depend on instinct to make them contract. But after you get fairly proficient at muscle use, you'll find that you can make those muscles start to work earlier and make them work more effectively by a few moments of effort, and then they will carry on all the way through your climax. It's just like the coordinated action you get when you empty your bladder—once you get started, a chain reaction takes over and you can hardly stop even if you want to."

After Maude was dressed, we got back to the details.

"The beauty of these particular exercises," I told her, "is that you don't have to waste a single minute while doing them. You can exercise while you're driving to the store or during the commercials on TV and nobody will know the difference. In fact, there's an advantage in linking them to some common everyday activity, because then you're more likely to get around to them every single day and to keep them up month after month and year after year. The point is that the exercises have to be continued to be fully effective in treating this condition; you can't let them slide after you get rid of your initial problem."

"But I can really change myself down there through exercises?"

"You certainly can. One doctor made actual measurements by attaching a bag of fluid inside the vagina to a pressure-measuring machine. Before exercises his patients couldn't budge the fluid column, but after a few weeks of effort they could squeeze down until the fluid pressure was quite high, which means that they could be in good, firm contact with a male organ inside, without strain or special thought. You might not be able to see any change in your contours when you are at rest, but exercises will make all the difference in the world when you're in action.

"Now let's get down to what you should do. Or maybe I had better start by telling you what *not* to do. You can increase the pressure inside your vagina slightly by straining as if you were having a bowel movement, but this increase comes from pressure exerted through the vaginal wall rather than from actual contraction of the pelvic or vaginal musculature. We're trying to make those organs play a more active part in your sex life, not merely to conduct pressure from some other source. You shouldn't have to grunt or strain in the least to get the proper effect if you're doing your exercises right.

"The muscles you need to strengthen act as a group to close your bladder, bowel, and sex openings and to lift the

pelvic floor. Usually they all work at once when you deliberately try to contract any one of them. So the best way
to get the vagina-squeezing muscles to contract is to use
the already-trained muscles which cut off the urinary
stream. Next time you void, just interrupt the flow two or
three times. You get a sort of lift-and-clamp-down sensation throughout the area when you do this, quite different
from the sensation of bearing down. After you've gotten
the general feel of the desired motion this way, try adding
a deliberate lifting or drawing-in action, as if you were
trying to pick up marbles with your vagina or to pull the
center of your pelvic floor or your rectum straight up into
your body. You'll find that one or another form of this
action gives even stronger contraction of the vaginal musculature. And that's about all there is to the exercises:
find the command that lets you tighten up those muscles,
then tighten them as strongly as you can for two or three
seconds. Let them relax for a few seconds and contract
them again eight or ten times in each exercise period. Try
to do this at least three times a day for the first six weeks to
get maximum buildup in the muscles, and at least once
a day thereafter. Use the same self-command to get muscular action started during intercourse whenever you think
you're ready, and let me know how you make out."

"And that's the whole story?"

"On the exercises, yes. And if you build up as much
muscular strength as I expect, you won't need to take any
further steps. There are two other measures which sometimes help in the meanwhile, though. First, lubrication.
People usually think of petroleum jelly (Vaseline is the
best-known brand) as a lubricant for use when things are
on the snug side, but actually it seems to help some women
with overly relaxed organs, too. The difference is in who
uses it and how. For snug-fitting organs, the *man* applies
a thin coat of *petroleum* jelly or the *woman* uses a liberal

amount of some *glycerine-base* product like K-Y jelly. For your relaxed organ, *you* should apply *petroleum* jelly fairly thickly and deep inside, so that it becomes tacky or gummy and makes the vagina cling to the inserted male organ as well as lubricating it. This approach is too messy for constant use, but might help you while you're getting started on your exercise program.

"Second, there's the matter of position. You probably settled on one basic sex posture in the first few months of marriage. In those days, your female organ was snug enough to make special postures not only unnecessary but also uncomfortable. You almost certainly wound up in a sex position which lines up the penis and vagina pretty much straight on. Now that there's more room down there, you'll find that you stay perfectly comfortable in positions where your husband enters at a considerable angle, and the angulation will help to make for more sexual friction. Try raising your legs so that your heels rest on his shoulders or lowering them so that he straddles one or both of your thighs. These positions usually make for snugger fit with a relaxed vagina, and might give you some help right away while you're still working on the exercises."

"And you're sure that will do the trick?"

"Practically. If you don't get all the help you need from these things, there is one other measure we can use before resorting to surgery. Some women who have let the pelvic muscles get very weak have a hard time getting started on exercises, and we have to help them by stimulating the muscles in the area electrically. Once they get enough strength to be able to feel the effects of muscle contraction, they can take over with ordinary exercise, so it usually takes only a few treatments. If you haven't seen some results in six to eight weeks, we'll give that approach a try, and there's always surgery as a last resort."

Last resorts didn't prove necessary for Maude Simms.

She reported substantial improvement in both her husband's and her own gratification after a few weeks of pelvic exercises. Having seen a great many women in similar straits, I believe that these particular maneuvers should be explained to every woman after each and every pregnancy, and that the main emphasis in postpartem care should be restored sexual capacity rather than maintained uterine position (the goal of knee-chest position and similar exercises normally prescribed). Some doctors might disagree about the importance of pelvic-floor-lifting exercises, but none can dispute their safety, convenience, and comfort. If there's any chance that they could help you both to give and to get more pleasure from your sex life, why not give them a try?

9. Infidelity

"It didn't mean a thing," Joe Pierce said. "Just a bit of secretarial fluff at a convention. You could blow her up tomorrow and I wouldn't even wince."

"You slept with her. That means something to *me*," his wife Florence countered. "Running down the girl won't do you any good. If she's such a dog, what does that make *me*, that you'll take her instead?"

"But you weren't *there*!" Joe said. "If you were there it never would have happened."

"You bet your life it wouldn't! But I'm not going to traipse around the country keeping you in line!"

"I don't think that's quite what he meant," I broke in.

121

"No, it isn't," Joe said. "And she knows damn well it isn't. What's the sense in this anyway, if all she wants to do is fight?"

"Now you're the one who's off the track," I said. "She didn't understand you, and it's a point we ought to get straight. Let's not fight about who's starting the fights, when we could be accomplishing something."

"What didn't she understand?"

"You said it never would have happened if she had been there."

"That's the truth. There wasn't anything to it. I just needed a little sex, that's all."

"And if Florence had been there?"

"If Flo was there we'd have had it and that would have been the end of it. But when there's nothing else around and you're feeling kind of horny, it's tough to let a chance go by. It didn't mean a thing—I mean not a thing. It was just sex, nothing personal—you know what I mean."

I nodded, then turned to Florence.

"Let's not get into what's right or wrong just yet. You two have very different points of view here, and the first thing is do you understand his?"

"Sure I understand it. If I step out on him that's horrible. If he steps out on me I'm the one who's wrong because I wasn't there. Well, who arranged it so I wasn't there in the first place? Who bought the tickets, eh?"

"Oh for heavens' sake!" Joe exclaimed. "Who's always griping about money? You wouldn't want to go to a convention, not for what it costs. You'd just be trading three days of boredom, mostly alone in a hotel room, for a good piece of our vacation, that's all."

"Maybe it's still cheaper if I go along—cheaper than hiring a detective to keep you in line."

"Look, you don't own me! I want to stay married or I

wouldn't be here. But you don't own me, and don't you forget it."

"What are you paying me for anyway," I broke in again, "to play audience to your fights or to try to work things out?"

"All right," Joe said. "Where were we?"

"We were trying to figure out why this outside affair means so little to you and so much to Florence—why you can't even understand why she's making such an issue of it and she can't understand what you mean when you say it has nothing to do with your marital relationship."

"So we look at it a little differently." Joe shrugged.

"You mean you don't give a damn about me, but you want me right there any time you feel in the mood."

"He didn't say that!" I rejoined. "You're both veering off all the time, and it's just because you don't talk the same language. Joe, you're using 'man talk.' Sex ends a body hunger, sex gives a guy some fun, love is something else again. When you have sex with someone you love, there's something pretty special about it because it's mutual and personal and more than just physical fun. You give each other everything you can. When you have it on the outside, it's just like grabbing a hot dog when you can't get home to dinner or sleeping in a motel if it's too far to your own house. You're meeting a need or satisfying an appetite, but there's no personal relationship involved: You are having sex, not making love, and to you there's quite a difference."

"That's right," Joe said. "She didn't mean a thing to me—it was just sex, that's all."

"Florence, you don't really understand that because you're used to 'girl talk.' Sex is the ultimate caress to you: a way of moving past friendship to love. To a woman, sex is always part of a relationship. That's why there are lots of gigolos who pretend love, but darn few men who get paid just for being good in bed. And that's why a woman who finds out her husband has had extramarital sex automatically feels that he has to be in love with the other woman. She uses her own viewpoint to color what goes on, and makes it quite a different thing from what it really is, at least so far as most relationships are concerned."

Florence thought for a moment.

"All right," she said, dabbing at her eyes with her handkerchief. "Maybe it isn't quite as big a thing as I made of it. But it still isn't right."

Tears trickled down her cheeks.

Joe twisted in his chair, not knowing whether or not to comfort her.

"Now I've made you angry," I said to Florence. "You think that I've sided with Joe because we're both men, and you're mad at me and mad at yourself for putting yourself in this position."

Florence looked at me defiantly. The tears dried up on the instant, but her lip quivered for a moment more. When she spoke, her voice was calm.

"But it still isn't right."

"I never said it was. You didn't deserve to be hurt, and Joe hurt you. But if you realize what happened—that this particular step out of line doesn't point to any deficiency in you or in the basic relationship you've built with Joe— it won't hurt *you* as badly. This particular incident is what we call a masturbation equivalent—Joe went out purely after physical pleasure and relief, not emotional comfort or love—rather than a true affair. It's still a slap in the face for you to some extent: Your femininity would be more perfectly proved if you met all his needs all of the time. But you can't downgrade yourself too much since you're his only real love object and the physical pressures only get ahead of you when he's off on trips."

"Look, you've left me way behind," Joe broke in. "A minute ago she was hurt so bad she's crying, then you said I hurt her when she didn't deserve it, now you're saying *she* fell down on the job but it wasn't all that bad. What's going on here anyway?"

"She didn't cry because she was hurt; she cried because she was mad. That's another difference between men and women that most people don't understand, and it's worth understanding because otherwise you do the wrong things and get the wrong reactions. When Florence cries because she's mad at you, the thing she wants the least is close contact with you, so if you try to take her in your arms and comfort her she probably just cries more. And when you think about it later and realize that you were just winning the argument or making your point, you think maybe she's turned on the tears to get her way, and that isn't right either. Just remember: When she cries she's angry."

"So how do you handle it when she's angry?"

"Try to figure out why. Most people—men *and* women this time—get angry because they feel threatened. Anger is your emotional stitch in time: It strikes out at the other guy whenever you see him getting close to your sore spots. But usually those sore spots are things you don't face consciously yourself. Like doubts about your sexual competence. Everybody has them: down deep, you wonder whether you're really good as a male sex partner and Florence wonders whether she's everything she should be as a woman. So the reason Florence got so mad at you, and the reason she was beginning to get mad at me, was because she felt that her own sexual self-confidence was under threat. *You* threatened her sexual self-confidence by your actions—by saying in effect 'you haven't met my needs, I've had to go elsewhere and even this pickup tart did something for me you can't'—and the threat became all the greater because she thought your need was for more *love* than she had given instead of for more physical relief. *I* threatened her sexual self-confidence by challenging her values—by saying that the way she has always thought of sex and love as intertwined might be right for her, but wasn't necessarily right for you or always right in your marriage."

Joe and Florence mulled these ideas over for a full minute, while I waited expectantly.

"I feel a little bit like crying now," Florence finally said. "But I don't dare." She smiled, and the atmosphere lightened.

"Still mad?" I asked.

"No. And you're right about one thing—I do cry when I'm angry."

"And I guess I've given you plenty to get mad at," Joe said.

"Which sounds like a good note on which to end this session," I said. "Except for just one thing. You both want to keep working at this marriage, don't you? It seems to me you've got real feeling for each other, and you ought to be able to get past this storm, but you've got to want it bad enough to work at it."

"Yes, I want it," Florence said first. "I don't know what I'd do without Joe, really."

Joe nodded, without taking his eyes off her, and I knew we were off to an excellent start.

When a woman is unfaithful to her husband, the affair almost always involves an emotional relationship. When a man is unfaithful to his wife, the incident can be purely physical, without any element of love. Many of these masculine incidents really do not mean anything. They do not involve any emotional or personal relationship and establish no conflict of loyalties or affection. This fact may not make them any more right or proper, but does make them easier to bear. Florence Pierce could not have lived comfortably with Joe as long as she felt that he had gone elsewhere for love. The implication that she had not met his full needs was too painful, and her defense against it (by striking back at him) too destructive. As it was, it took weeks of upheaval, and Joe paid a fierce price for his few moments of illicit pleasure, but ultimately the Pierces got back on an even keel.

Affairs with emotional as well as physical elements cause a somewhat more difficult situation.

"I suppose I'll have to leave him," Janet Iverson said. "There's nothing else I can do."

She sat with downcast eyes, twisting her handkerchief and shifting frequently in her chair.

"Why?" I asked.

"He's having an affair with his secretary. In fact, he checked into a motel with her yesterday afternoon."

"How do you know?"

"One of my neighbors saw him. And I went there myself. He was there, all right. I saw his car outside."

"Quite a shock for you."

"It certainly was! I just didn't know what to do. I drove around for a while, then called and made this appointment."

"Without saying anything to your husband?"

"That's right. But I'll have to leave him. Won't I?"

"Do you really want to?"

She fidgeted with her handkerchief for a moment.

"I guess I don't. But isn't that the right thing to do?"

I shrugged. "There's no hard-and-fast rule. Let's look at a few alternatives. First of all, do you want a divorce?"

I paused, but she didn't answer.

"If so, you can probably get it, and get a good financial settlement as well. Most of your friends will commiserate with you, and nobody will blame you for what has happened. But you'll wind up alone and starting all over as far as finding a husband again—if you *want* to have a husband."

"I do. I'm not much for a career or anything. And Steve hasn't been bad either. I really don't want to leave him, if I can work things out. Can't I face him with this and tell him he's got one more chance? One more break and that's the end?"

"You can," I said noncommittally. "That's one way to use the incident—to make him toe the line. Once you use something like this as a club, though, you don't know quite which way things will turn. How do you think Steve would take it?"

"Well, if he loved me. . . ."

"He'd put his tail between his legs and come home. But what would that do to him? How would he feel about taking your orders, and being faced constantly with ultimatums?"

"I see what you mean. Steve would probably stick with me, but he'd hate me for making him crawl."

"And how would *you* feel about it?"

She thought for a minute. "I'd think less of him for knuckling under," she said. "Steve's always been the strong one. I don't know how we'd get along with me giving orders."

"Does *he* give the orders, then?"

"Not really. But I sort of depend on him to make the decisions and take care of things, if you know what I mean."

"I think so. As I understand it, then, there's not much room in your pattern for the use of clubs and compulsion.

I mean, in your present framework there's just not any way you can use the fact that you caught him off base."

"No, there really isn't. But maybe we need a new framework. Maybe that's what's wrong."

"Maybe. At least something's wrong or Steve wouldn't have roved."

"Wrong with me?"

"Not necessarily. Although it doesn't really matter. If you've really decided not to use Steve's transgression as a weapon, what difference does it make who's at fault? The important thing is where you can go from here, and the past only matters if you can learn from it."

"I haven't learned much so far. Just that I can't trust my husband, I guess."

"We're not talking about trust. Trust would be the key if you were writing a contract: You'd stay with him if he toed the line, and you wouldn't really be able to tell whether he toed the line unless you could trust him. But we've already thrown out that approach. The question isn't whether he'll obey a new promise better than he obeyed the old ones. The question is whether there's any way for you to ease the pressures that kept him from obeying the old ones. Whether he yielded to those pressures because of his weakness, because of outside temptation, or because of your failure to meet his needs doesn't really matter. What matters is that he did yield, and that to keep him from yielding some more you either have to relieve the pressure or strengthen him against it."

"I don't understand."

"When a man roves, he's generally trying to meet a need that isn't being met at home. Maybe the need is something special to him, maybe it's not. It really doesn't matter, as long as we're trying to find a cure instead of fixing blame. The crucial point is that if you meet all his needs at home, the outside affair will die on the vine."

"How do I do that?"

"What do you think? If you were setting out to make Steve one hundred percent happy without concern for coming out even or getting your share, is there anything you would do differently?"

"Well. . . ."

"Why don't you think about it, send up a few trial balloons, and let me talk with you again next week."

She started for the door, then turned.

"You're sure?" she said.

"Sure of what?"

"That if I do everything I can to make Steve happy this other affair will fade out of the picture?"

"No, I can't be sure of that. But I'm sure it's your best chance, and that it *ought* to work. You met all his needs for years: physical, emotional, social, the whole works. The odds are that you can meet them again if you really try, and if you do I'm sure that the other woman won't look very good to him anymore."

Janet Iverson might well have put her marriage back together through pressure and negotiations, leaning heavily on Steve's sense of obligation, his responsibility to her and the children. If she had, it would have been a "contract marriage," more like a business partnership than a working team. She chose to try for an improved relationship instead. While her decision might seem a bit "turn the other cheek," she adopted the approach mainly because it was most likely to bring her marriage back to the basis she wanted, and actually it did. Janet didn't ask for any further help with the specifics. Once she decided to make an all-out effort to keep her husband happy instead of trying to club him back into line, she knew pretty much what to do—and she really didn't need further counseling.

She kept in touch with me, though, and told me a year or so later that everything had come out all right. In fact, while it may seem strange in a society which expects such "cheated" wives to be outraged, she honestly feels that her marriage is sounder now than it was before.

Don't get me wrong. I'm not advocating an end to sexual loyalty in marriage. My point is that men or women who find crucial needs (whether physical or emotional) unmet within their marriage develop a distorted point of view and eroded values. The mistress or cuckolding lover looks good mainly to the emotionally deprived. Older and deeper ties almost always reassert themselves if the deprivation stops, and this way of handling the situation generally draws the couple closer instead of driving them apart. This is not to fix the blame on the "depriver," either. A great many affairs result from special needs which the spouse cannot anticipate and does not see until the affair brings them to light. It simply means: "If your relationship is important, try to improve it instead of putting it to further trial as is."

One surprising point about this way of handling affairs is that most couples discuss the situation later. When the offending party senses that his spouse will say: "I'm glad I could help you through it" instead of "How could you?" he or she almost always brings the matter up. And at that point the whole business becomes another trial you have withstood together instead of a wedge driven between you.

"We never did anything wrong," Sophie Carlson said tearfully. "Lars knows that."

"I know you never went to bed together," Lars Carlson said. "But how can I go on loving someone who's always mooning around over somebody else? It's just about killed all the feeling I have for her."

"I know," Sophie said. "It's all my fault. But what could

I do? I didn't *want* to fall in love with him—it just happened."

As we talked further, the story came out. The Carlsons had been married twenty-two years, with three children now almost grown. After the children were all in school, Sophie became bored. She enrolled in an Art Institute pottery-making course, and became intrigued with both the art and the professor. In the beginning she acknowledged the first but not the second preoccupation, even to herself. But gradually the facts forced themselves upon her. She had taken every course offered, and still enrolled again just to be near the teacher; personal contact spread outside classroom hours to luncheons and other friendly public liaisons and finally to apartment visits ("All innocent— just being together"). Suddenly Sophie realized that she was "in love for the first time, really. When I married Lars I knew he'd be easy to live with and a good provider, but I never loved him." Alternately consumed with guilt and "so sorry for myself that I cried and cried," Sophie went on for five years, never breaking off the affair and never consummating it.

According to Lars, she "rubbed my nose in the dirt. Every word she said amounted to saying I couldn't stand up to the other fellow as a man." One day as she was "crying and carrying on, talking to this guy on the telephone," Lars walked over, broke the connection, and asked for a divorce.

The Carlsons came to my office several times to hash things out. Sophie's discontent, guilt, and agitation seemed at least partly due to depression, and I hoped that the pills I prescribed might help get her on a more even keel. Perhaps three or four years earlier such a step might have brought about a reconciliation, but things had gone too far. Ultimately Lars and Sophie were divorced.

If your mate goes elsewhere for love, you feel serious doubt about your powers of fulfillment. You are hit right to the core: Your capacities as a *person*, not simply as a provider or a housekeeper or even as a sex partner, are suddenly subject to doubt. You may not be conscious of this fact—your mind may protect you from it—but you react to it in one way or another. You become angry or depressed or a bit disconnected—all harmful responses.

If you find that your mate has strayed, you almost automatically try to fix the blame fully on him because the idea that you may have failed to meet vital needs and thus contributed to the difficulty is too painful to face. Having fixed the blame, you tend to lash out, to punish, to break off relations. Blame-fixing, whether the burden rests on you, your spouse, or on the third party, never really helps to solve the situation. Yet the only person who can keep from making this the major issue usually proves to be the injured party. If you ever find yourself playing that role, you will probably come out best in the long run if you sit on your hands, try to calm down, and base your approach on preserving your marriage instead of protecting your self-esteem at the price of a lost or damaged relationship.

10. Questions of Conscience

"The longer we're married, the less she wants to do with sex," Morton Abrams complained. "We're down to maybe twice a month, and then it's like pulling teeth."

"Why not?" his wife Judy replied. "If I made it easy, you'd be at it all the time. And I don't get that much out of it."

"That's right, doctor. She doesn't enjoy sex at all."

"So I'm not the passionate type," Judy said with a shrug. "I can live with it. Mort's the one who's making the complaints."

"That's right," he said calmly. "And I'm the one who's paying the bills. But it's up to you, doctor. There's our problem: It's no fun for her, and she thinks I'm some kind of sex-crazy monster when I want her more than twice a month. Now you tell us where to start."

"Let's get a little fuller picture first," I said. Turning to Judy, I went on: "Tell me a little more about how you feel when you can see a sexual situation starting to develop."

"Sleepy. It's every night, you know. All I've got to do is roll between the sheets and he's nuzzling away."

I shook my head admiringly.

"What a sense of humor!" I said. "But it can get you in trouble sometimes. I might be able to help you if you didn't make a joke of your real feelings. Are you ashamed of sex? Afraid?"

"What's to be ashamed of? We're married."

"And that makes everything all right?"

"So he tells me every night."

"But you don't quite agree."

"No, if you really want to know." Suddenly she was angry. "Marriage makes it all right to make love. But he isn't making love, he's satisfying the beast in him. It's just nice, warm meat to him, and who the hell cares! That's all he wants out of *this* deal, too—something a little warmer for himself, something a little better, maybe with a brand new bag of tricks. Well, I'm not having any! I'm getting out of here right now."

She jerked her coat on and actually started for the door.

"Whew!" I said. "I really hit a nerve that time, didn't I?"

Suddenly she began to weep.

"It's just that he never pays any attention to me," she said. "Not as a woman—as somebody to love. All he wants is for me to lie there like some whore and just *let him.* And that isn't right—that just can't be right."

"What do you mean right?"

"Why quibble about details? Is just isn't right!"

But we did get into details in a solo interview a few weeks later. The subject came up during a discussion of pride, specifically what should make a woman proud of herself.

"What's a woman supposed to do?" Judy asked. "She can't prove herself by going to work—most people figure a career woman as having taken second best. She's supposed to keep her husband happy and play second fiddle and raise lovely kids; only if she keeps her husband happy everyone says how lucky she is to marry someone so even-tempered, and if she plays second fiddle nobody even notices her, and by the time the kids are old enough to prove how they've turned out she's got one foot in the grave."

"That's right," I said. "If you wait for outside recognition, you'll still be waiting when they take you away. You've got to form a little mutual admiration society right inside your own self."

"How's that?"

"You've got to pat yourself on the back once in a while, whenever you have any reason at all to feel that you deserve it. And you've got to give yourself points whenever you measure up to a passing grade, too. Don't kick yourself for missing an 'A' average."

"So I pat myself on the back for keeping up the house, managing the budget, dressing neat, and reading the newspapers. What happens if I flunk a required subject like sex?"

"What do you mean, flunk?"

"Fail, flop, collapse, miss the mark, fold in a heap! It's gotten where I funk out just at the thought of it. If that's not an 'F' grade, what is?"

"What do *you* think? What kind of curve are you grading on?"

"What's the difference? Whatever the numbers, I fail. It's never been right with me, not once."

"Right?"

"Like it should be. Where I get the full response. Or any response at all, since our honeymoon turned out to be a flop."

"Then your lack of response is what keeps it from being right?"

"Mort acts like marriage was season-ticket prostitution. He pays the bills, and I warm the bed whether I'm the least bit interested or not."

"Yes, I can see how you might look at it that way. But the key point is that you think it isn't right unless you're interested—passionately involved you might say. And by 'right' you don't just mean right for *you*—giving you all you're entitled to—you mean *right*, proper, morally defensible, and acceptable to your conscience. Is that so?"

"Let me think about that. . . . So what's wrong with it? If we're both getting thrills and satisfaction, it's making love and that's *right*. If I'm not getting a thing out of it, I'm giving to get—giving *myself* to get groceries or special consideration or what have you."

"So you feel as if you're selling yourself every time you have intercourse without passion—without full passionate reward, in fact."

"I guess so. What's the difference between making a living as a whore and letting Mort crawl all over me for my monthly housekeeping check? You can't call that making love. It's nothing but season-ticket prostitution."

"You love that phrase, don't you?"

"No, I hate it!" She began to weep. "That's what I've felt like for months, a lowdown season-ticket whore! But I just don't know what to do. I love Mort, really I do, and I've tried and tried but nothing happens and it isn't right and the more I try the worse it gets. . . ." She sobbed more and more heavily.

"So you went on your honeymoon, and nothing good happened. Right away you started to fret and feel guilty and deficient and mad all at once. Why didn't you give yourself a chance?"

"What do you mean?"

"Do you know any woman who enjoyed her first sexual encounter? It's physically uncomfortable, emotionally upsetting, and mentally disturbing all at once. You've got to love the fellow very much (and get the kind of gentle handling that comes when he loves you) just to get through it without a disaster. And the next one isn't much better, or the next. A woman can get something out of early episodes, but only if she can stay relaxed and feel comfortable about what she's doing. If she thinks she's demeaning herself every time she has sex for *him* instead of to satisfy her own passion, then she's making sex a can of worms and nothing else. Because she'll never get enough emotional good out of the act for full response to develop. She'll go the downhill spiral instead of the uphill one, the way you have."

"I didn't expect much the first time, really. But I thought—I mean shouldn't I have gotten *something* before the honeymoon was over?"

"If you mean the honeymoon *trip,* darn few wives ever reach a climax in the first few weeks. If you mean the honeymoon *period*—the blissful, noncritical phase when you can depend on the good feeling engendered by newly requited love to smooth out all differences—that obviously didn't amount to much for you. If you mean the honeymoon in sexologic terms, you have hardly started.

"When a woman starts her sexual experience, the physical sensations she gets are far from pleasant. If she checks to see whether her hymen is unusually tough, uses adequate lubrication, and gets reasonably considerate handling from her partner, she can get through her early experiences without great discomfort. But it's never pure joy. In these early incidents, the only pleasures she gets come through her relationship with her partner. She shares his pleasure to some extent, as she would share the emotions in any experience with someone she loves, and she feels proud and happy to have brought fulfillment—to have proved her ability to please a partner, and particularly a partner she loves. These *plus* feelings link themselves in her mind with the sensations of intercourse, and add the kind of emotional color she needs to become fully responsive.

"That's the sexologist's kind of honeymoon period: the time when a woman takes part in sex without much hope of immediate passionate reward, but because love drives her to please her partner, lets her share his pleasure, and makes her success in satisfying him a source of confidence and contentment. That's what you've missed, because the idea of making love without feeling passionate was so hateful to you that you couldn't remain emotionally at ease and reasonably free from hostility, anxiety, and guilt. And that's the honeymoon period you've got to experience before you'll develop full responsiveness. There simply has to be a period when you participate in sex fairly freely for the sake of emotional benefits other than climax-producing excitement. That period might be fairly short now, since the physical changes of the original honeymoon are over, or it might stretch on for months or years while you grapple with the residues of this period of turmoil. But you will never go from where you are to passionate responsiveness without some sex without passion, with a partner for whom you have feeling."

"You mean with Mort?"

I shrugged. "You say you love him. You've gone through a lot together. Those things mean more than 'compatibility.' I'm convinced that most women who fail with their first partners and find success with someone else simply went through the adaptive process before they reached the final man on their list instead of finding the one man on earth who would have suited them. Of course the whole sexologic honeymoon phase doesn't have to be spent with one man for response to develop. Some women even get their main satisfaction in early incidents through proof of their attractions and become responsive through multiple conquests. Others get satisfaction from pleasing almost anyone who pays any attention to them. But most women find that deep ties give them the best chance for shared pleasure and prideful womanhood, and that deep ties aren't particularly easy to form and break."

"Well, I guess old Mort's all right. But I'll still feel a little like a whore, giving in when I'm not so inclined."

"Maybe you will—ideas like that die hard. But sex as an act of loving service is a long shot from prostitution in my book. In fact, the shoe may even be on the other foot. Mutual passion is tit-for-tat, where you do what you do for the sake of what you'll get out of it. Trying to please a man when you're not much in the mood is pure loving service, with everything you do aimed mainly at either his pleasure or the future of your relationship. Which is the greater act of love really? The act of selfish animal desire or that of unselfish giving?"

Judy's "sexologic honeymoon" lasted only a few weeks, after which she reported satisfying communion with increasing frequency. I kept in touch for almost a year, at the end of which time things seemed to be going reasonably well. We had occasional conferences, but none of the deep psychological probing type. Judy managed to resolve the situation by discussing the crucial ideas of the moment without much exploration of where she got them.

A generation ago, psychologists found many women afflicted with the "madonna-prostitute dichotomy"—the idea that a woman had to be either good or sexually responsive and could never be both at once. That notion has largely disappeared. But the idea which plagued Judy has replaced it. The passion-prostitution dichotomy—that a woman participates in sex either because of urgent passionate desire or for hope of gain and that no other motives are possible—grips most girls at some stage of their upbringing. When combined with exaggerated hopes for the honeymoon, this idea imposes a great burden of guilt and anxiety which harm both sex life and marriage.

The only antidote is factual information. A woman's early sexual experience virtually never gives passionate delight, and response often takes years to develop. Almost every woman engages in intercourse without being driven by passion at least occasionally during the early years, and most marriages involve at least a few such episodes throughout the years. Such willing surrender for the benefit of your partner and your marriage is completely different from prostitution and actually is a very potent demonstration of love. As a necessary part of marriage, such sexual service gets and deserves full approval by law, by all recognized faiths, and by our general moral and ethical codes. Why then should any woman feel guilty about it?

When you were very young and impressionable, you had only a vague idea of sexual relations. But you had very specific experience with modesty. People laid down the law on what body parts you could expose to view. They reinforced their rules both with example and by shaming you whenever you strayed into areas regarded as taboo.

No wonder so many women (and quite a few men) have sexual hangups related to self-exposure rather than to intercourse itself. After being trained for twenty years to conceal their private parts from members of the opposite sex, why shouldn't they feel guilt and anxiety about sharing bedroom, bath, and bed? Almost everyone has at least some problems associated with modesty at the start of his sex life, and quite a few develop truly major difficulties on this basis.

"I'm sending you a real lulu," Dr. B said over the telephone. "Name of Mary Ann Schulz. This gal broke down and cried at her six-weeks checkup when I told her she could get back to sex. 'For God's sake don't tell my husband!' she said. Can you imagine it?"

"Afraid so," I said. "But tell me more—any physical problems?"

"Lord, no. From what she tells me, it's been like this right from the start. You can't blame my delivery—it's strictly in your department."

Mary Ann showed up a few days later, in a high-neckline, simple-style dress. When I asked her what I could do for her, she said:

"Dr. B sent me."

"Yes?"

"It's something to do with—didn't he talk to you?"

"Yes, but I want to know how *you* see the problem."

"Well, it has to do with our marriage." She paused for a moment, then tumbled on. "We just don't get along well in our marital relations. You know what I mean."

A great many people have difficulty using straightforward language with regard to sex. How many times do you use the word "it" for sexual intercourse, for instance? Or some other euphemistic phrase?

Inability to talk frankly about sex makes husband-wife communication much more stilted, and adds an anxiety to sex that does nothing but harm. Fortunately, the inhibitions involved usually prove quite brittle. Students in classes where "desensitization exercises" are carried out repeat together phrases like "sexual intercourse," "vagina," and "penis" after the teacher a few times, and usually find that they never again become embarrassed about using these words. But this hardly seemed the apt starting point with Mary Ann, and so I didn't confront her with it. We went into relatively innocuous information instead: married three years, one child now two months old, no substantial frictions in any sphere but sex. Which brought us back to her original complaint.

"Everything seemed just fine before we were married. We never went all the way, but we got along all right. But then we got married, and I don't know what went wrong."

"On the honeymoon?"

"Yes. Even our wedding night. We had intercourse, all right, but it seemed to terrify me. Even before he came into the room I was scared to death, huddled in under the blankets and shivering all the while."

"You had a pretty hard time, then."

"I just couldn't relax. I can't ever seem to relax. And it's getting worse instead of better. It's been so bad so often that I can hardly stand to think about it."

"That's not unusual—once things start going wrong, you always get further anxiety tied into the picture. But let's go back to the early period—after your honeymoon, after you had a little chance to get used to each other. Did you have intercourse only at night or sometimes in the morning or afternoon?"

"Oh, only at night. I couldn't think of it in the daytime. That would be—well I don't know."

"And always with the lights out?"

"Of course."

"I see." I paused for a moment. "You know, most couples have intercourse sometimes in the daytime hours, especially before they have children. And most of them like a little light once in a while, so that they can see each other's faces."

Mary Ann shuddered. "I just couldn't stand it with the lights on."

"It sounds to me as if you were brought up rather strictly with regard to modesty."

"Oh, yes. Jim's folks just run in and out like it was nothing—I have to practically post a guard in front of the bathroom door when I go there—but it was never like that at my house. You didn't let anybody see you in your underwear, much less in the nude. I never saw my parents undressed—either my father or my mother. I don't think I even saw them in a bathrobe, at least not without pajamas or something underneath."

"And that's the way they taught you?"

"I suppose so. I can't remember anybody *saying* anything. Mom tells me that a neighbor boy started to take down my panties once and everybody got in a furor, but mostly it was just the way things were done. That's one of the main reasons I'm here: I've got a little girl now, and I'd hate to have her turn out the way I am."

"I wondered about that. It must have been hard for you to come here."

"I wouldn't have done it just for me. This is the way I am, that's all. But she doesn't ever have to be this way, if I can figure out how it happened."

After six or eight rather fruitless conferences, Mary Ann felt willing to get into the matter of sex technique. In the clinical setting, with drapes covering all but one area of her body and with Jim right in the room, we started a discussion of what caresses, movements, and stimulations were apt. Mary Ann showed herself to Jim part by part, down to the inner portions of her genitals, and he did the same with her. And when it was all over she remarked in amazement: "Why there was nothing to it!"

Two weeks later she had her first orgasm, and her follow-up reports have been favorable ever since.

Exposure-related anxieties have a great deal to do with frigidity, impotence and other sexual difficulties, almost entirely because modesty is taught in a way which makes the taboos apply to everyone, and which carries implications of dirtiness, nastiness, and shame.

People raised in more open households generally remain free from such hangups. In such households, children learn not to expose their private parts *outside the family,* but there is no concern about self-exposure within the family group, no feeling of embarrassment if one family member walks in while another is changing his clothes or taking a bath. Such free movement soon becomes a part of family togetherness, making "private parts" *precious* secret instead of shameful. This attitude, reinforced by daily practice, helps everyone in the household—the parents by freeing them of troublesome anxieties and the youngsters by providing a more favorable basis for later marriage.

"It never happened every time," Linda Case said. "But I used to come pretty often, and here lately it's practically not at all."

"How long have you been having trouble?" I asked.

"That's hard to say. It's been sort of a gradual change over the past five years. But there's one thing rather funny about it: I can respond just fine when we're away on a trip. George even kids me about it—says I'm a victim of airline advertising, and that's why I can't get romantic except in Hawaii or something."

"That's interesting."

"What makes it even funnier is that I used to be just the reverse. At least George claims that I'd never respond when we were *away* from home the first few years, and he used to be hardly able to wait till he could get me back to our own bed. But I don't really remember that."

"When does he mean? Right after you were married?"

"Then and for the first few years after we had the children. Of course our trips were different then—mostly we'd go to see his family or mine, or else we'd take a cabin someplace with the youngsters. We never really used to get off by ourselves in those days—didn't have the money, for one thing."

"I suppose when you went to visit, the houses got a little crowded."

"Oh yes, but we always had a bedroom to ourselves. I mean we didn't have much privacy, with those thin walls and stuff—you could always hear just what was going on all through the house—but we had a place to ourselves. Same way with the cabins—we never slept in the same room with the children. I wouldn't have it."

The pattern of Linda's difficulty already was falling into place. She responded sexually when she and her husband were totally alone and thoroughly insulated from other people. When anyone else might hear the bedsprings squeak, Linda went into a freeze. Like most people with extreme inhibition about having others know about their sexual activity, Linda's problem became most acute when other generations were under the same roof: she couldn't relax for sex when her parents or in-laws were in the same house with her, and as soon as her children reached an age when they might be aware she developed the same pattern with them.

I didn't raise this issue bluntly at an early stage of our acquaintance, but as the conference was drawing to a close I steered the conversation toward a related topic.

"I'm a little foggy on your household arrangements," I said. "What kind of provisions have you made for privacy? Where is the master bedroom in relation to the others, for instance?"

"Oh, the bedrooms are all together. I've always been worried that the children might get sick in the night or something."

"I suppose you sort of sleep with one ear open, then, like most mothers."

"Yes I do. George says I'm up before they take their first breath after a cry—lots of times he's awake reading or something and still can't get to them before I wake out of a sound sleep."

"Sort of housewife's radar, eh? So I guess you keep the bedroom door open."

"It's never closed at night. I wouldn't think of it."

"Then don't you think privacy might be a factor in your sex problem? Lots of people find even a vague risk of being interrupted sets them on edge."

"I've never thought of it."

"Not consciously, perhaps. But that's the kind of concern that often eats at you under the surface. Let's see— your youngest is six years old now. I'm sure you would hear him all right through a closed door."

"Oh, but I wouldn't do that!"

"Why not?"

"Then the children would know what was going on." She actually shuddered.

"Then they don't know what is going on now?"

"Of course not. But if I started closing the bedroom door they'd know *something* was going on—or at least I would worry about it."

"More than you do now, with the bedroom door open?"

"Well—I don't know. It does sound silly when you think about it."

"All right. We'll talk about this more next time, when George is here with you. But in the meanwhile I'd like to see you close that bedroom door. In fact, what I would *really* like to see you do is buy one of the intercom sets that you can plug into the different sockets in your home and set it up so you can hear the children at night, but they can't possibly hear you. Then you can close the bedroom door, and lock it if you have to, without feeling as if you're the least bit out of touch."

Linda returned with her husband George a couple of weeks later. When I asked them how things were coming, George answered:

"You've helped her, doctor. We didn't get the intercoms —the kids are old enough that we could hear them anyway—but that bedroom door business did help her to relax."

"Good," I said. "Then let's go on the assumption that *privacy* makes a big difference, and see if we can get some idea of why."

"Isn't that natural?" Linda asked.

"Not to the point where the idea that someone might know what is going on upsets you so much you can't get anything at all out of sex."

"But I just can't relax under those circumstances. In fact, even with the door closed and the kids sound asleep I'm still listening all the time with one ear to see if they might be stirring."

"I know. So let's try to figure out why you're so hung up on this point. First of all I'm sure you think it would do the children tremendous harm if they happened in while you were having intercourse."

I paused to let them comment, but neither did.

"That's what almost everyone thinks. In fact, most people I talk with seem to think that it's only natural to insulate children from any evidence of their parents' continuing activity in the sexual sphere."

"That's right," George said. "You just don't let them know about it."

"That's the customary attitude—but there's good reason to think it's a harmful remnant of Victorian prudery. Certainly it isn't natural in the sense of being universal. Ours is one of the only generations and one of the only cultures in which housing has ever allowed this degree of privacy for the majority of the people. Our pioneer grandparents had sex in log cabins with the youngsters in the open attic above, and the Eskimos certainly don't kick their young out into the sixty below every time they get passionate!"

"I see what you mean," George said. "But isn't it a step up?"

"For the couple, yes. Sex deserves your full attention, and other people around—even sleeping children—offer some distraction. If nothing else, they limit your expression to silent forms. But what about the children? I just can't find any reason for the idea that they will be severely damaged if they happen in while you are having intercourse, and I haven't found a psychiatrist yet who recalled a case in which such an experience seemed crucial. Nobody recommends that you go out of your way to have your children observe you, but if an accident happens there is no evidence that it will do any harm.

"And there are sound reasons why awareness (not *observation*) of continuing parental sex life should help instead of hurt. One of the main sources of trouble for youngsters today is the idea that sex is strictly the province of the young. We tell them sex is all important, let them think it's virtually over by age twenty-five, then wring our hands in horror when they hasten off to try it. Every generation repeats the story of the dried beans—that if you put a bean in the jar every time you have intercourse for the first year and take one out every time thereafter, you'll never get the jar empty—and parents don't let their own example prove to their children that it's a despicable lie. In actual fact, most couples get the most out of sex in their thirties. Most of them get considerably more out of it in their forties than they did in their twenties, and there are substantial gratifications on into the fifties, sixties, and even seventies. Almost half the healthy men and women over eighty who have a willing partner can still enjoy sex. The long haul is a lot more important than a young start, but most of society adheres to the opposite myth. So your only chance of getting your own children to see it the right way is by example."

"You mean actually tell them that we sleep together for the sake of having sex?"

"You don't really have to tell them if you just don't join the conspiracy of falsehood and omission. When your six-year-old asks when he's going to have a new brother or sister, don't say: 'We're done with all that.' Say 'Whenever we think we can afford it.' And if the older children are around it wouldn't hurt to say: 'It would have happened a long time ago if it weren't for birth control.' Go ahead with your kisses and caresses whether the children are around or not. What's wrong with going as far in public *married* as you did when you were just *engaged*? And in

conversation. You know that if you had other adults in
the house with whom you were half as familiar as you are
with your youngsters, you would make direct or oblique
references to the pleasures of your bed several times each
week. You would discuss your 'second honeymoon,' compare the comforts of your bed with the conditions prevail-
ing for youthful or illicit love, commemorate your changes
in mood after making physical love, and so forth. Why not
forget the notion that you have to talk differently when in
the company of the young? As long as they are truly innocent, your remarks will go over their heads, and when
knowledge begins to dawn they'll appreciate that sex remains part of marriage for many years."

"Maybe something like that would be all right," George
said.

"That's all you really need to do. I've never suggested
selling bedside seats. But if you just let the light dawn,
you'll be surprised at how soon youngsters do develop
basic awareness. All five of my youngsters were pretty well
clued in by the time they were ten, and when they were in
their teens they gave my wife a black negligee with a card
that read 'For research.' "

"And that didn't bother you?" Linda asked.

"Not at all. In fact, I've seen several further advantages
from this kind of openness. When the youngsters know
that your relationship is a total one—mental, emotional,
and physical—they have a much better model on which
to base their own man-woman relations. The three youngsters we've already raised to adulthood have all followed in
our footsteps in forming deep and apparently sound relationships with their husbands or wives. And we've had less
generation gap than any other household I know. Our
grown-up youngsters treat us like one of the gang. They
ask our counsel, too, partly because they know we won't

take over their prerogatives but mostly, I think, because they consider us experienced people with similar alignment to their own instead of old fogies who are out of it."

"Of course, you're sort of special in this department—what makes you think it would work the same way for anyone else?"

"I've had a few patients who've been able to try it. I could tell you about several families which have opened up new roads of communication between teenagers and adults just by being frank about adult sex and adult relationships—by providing example rather than just regulation. Incidentally, several of these cases have demonstrated another point: when youngsters know about parental sex, they feel differently about inside-the-family competition for their mother's or father's love. Neurotic thinking assumes that daughter must compete with mother for the father's love, and son with father for the mother's. This is the basic stress of family life, according to Freud and his followers, and it tends to disappear when the youngsters recognize the qualitative difference between the sexual husband-wife relationship and the asexual parent-child one. Actually, your love for each other makes it easier for you to love your children, not harder. A child who understands the difference between varieties of love easily grasps this point and ceases to feel that he has to compete with one of his own parents for the other one's love."

"You mean that if our children know we're making physical love it might actually *help* them mentally as well as in their relationship with us?"

"Absolutely. If the youngsters have been thinking neurotically and feel jealousy, there might be trouble—but that will mean an undesirable situation which already exists has been brought out in the open, not that an undesirable situation has been created. And that hasn't hap-

pened in any one of the families I've seen through this
change. It's just been one more barrier of phoniness
removed, and one more actually obvious fact brought into
the open. In fact, it's basically rather strange that so many
youngsters can possibly be deluded on this point: I've
seen high school seniors show obvious astonishment at the
idea that their parents were having intercourse regularly
even when they had baby brothers at home. It's a crazy set
of values—to conceal all signs of making love while you
let kids hear you bicker and fight, to hide continuing sex
when you want them to plan for the long pull, to pretend
you're over the hill when you want them to look to you
for counsel, and to conceal the thing that makes your love
for each other different from that you have for them when
you want them to recognize this point. It doesn't make
sense, except that everybody does it."

All this while, Linda sat by almost as a spectator. She
didn't argue, she didn't protest, she didn't show obvious
emotional response. Throughout the rest of the interview,
she remained distracted and deep in thought. But George
called a few days later to cancel our next appointment,
and a few months later reported that their problem was
at an end.

What about you? Can you romp freely with an open
door between your children and your bed? If not, you
might sit down together with your husband or wife and
talk out your privacy values. Go over the matter for yourself, study the pros and cons, and see if you don't come
up with the same conclusion I've reached long ago: If you
close and lock the bedroom door, your children will
probably know what is going on, but it won't hurt them
one single solitary bit.

11. Identity Conflicts

"But you've had erections sometime," I said to Harold Mason (who was the father of three children).

"Not really," Harold said. "At least my penis never has stood sturdy like it should." He made a gesture with his forearm and clenched fist.

"Never—right from the start?"

"That's right. I was big man on campus, class president and all the rest, with practically my choice of dates all swooning over me. But the only time I ever got one of them to the point of giving in, I just couldn't get anywhere. Then Louise and I were married, and our honeymoon was a complete fiasco. Louise was practically panting

for it, and I just hung there loose. So she cried and called
me a bunch of dirty names, and we've been at it ever since."

"I gather you've ruled out physical causes."

"Sure. I've been to half a dozen urologists, and none of
them could find anything."

"And you get erections all right at other times? Wet
dreams, masturbation, early morning when your bladder
is full?"

"That's what really fries me. I wake up hard as a rock,
and if I grab Louise without hardly giving her a chance
I'll finish bang-bang like a rabbit, and next thing you
know we've got another child. But if I take time even to
kiss her, it begins to fade away."

Harold had been the youngest of several children and
always a go-getter. At age eleven he bought his own
clothes with earnings from his enterprises. He stayed busy
all the time, partly "so that I wouldn't have to stay around
the house."

Harold had a vehement antipathy toward his mother,
who he said "didn't want me, didn't like me, and didn't
hardly speak to me if she could help it." He had never
seen any demonstration of affection between his parents,
and branded his father "a nothing—just a walking zilch."
His description of a family breakfast was quite revealing.
"My father wanted cream for his cereal, but he wasn't
talking to anybody at the time, so he couldn't ask for it.
He just sat there. None of us knew what he wanted—we
didn't know quite what to do. So finally we all ate. He
stayed at his place fuming until everybody was finished,
then stormed out of the house. It wasn't till the same thing
happened two or three times that my sister figured out
what he wanted: It was right there on the table, but he
wouldn't reach for it. Then when he went into his act she

passed him the cream and everything was all right. But he didn't thank her or anything even then."

In that sterile, loveless, hostility-ridden atmosphere, Harold attached nothing but negative values to man-woman relations. What he learned about womankind from living with his mother was enough to set him off the breed for life; he never did manage to treat a woman as a love object. The model of manhood his father gave was weak-spined and hostile. And the man-woman relationship he observed ranged from icy noncommunication to mutual rage. The only good thing about the situation was the diversion of energies Harold managed to achieve—his urges to assert and prove himself were denied the normal sexual outlets and settled into business-related drive. He was a highly productive and successful citizen in every other field except sex and marriage, where he remained a failure despite my efforts and the labors of several psychiatrists over a period of many years.

Harold came out of his childhood equally mad at both sexes. He couldn't see a woman as a love object—but neither could he see a man in this role. This fact, aided by his freedom to vent his spleen, push people around, and still earn both respect and allegiance in the world of business, probably kept Harold from becoming a homosexual. At least, modern psychiatric theory holds that homosexuality results in large part from sufficiently negative feelings towards one's mother (or other dominant female figure in early life) that acceptance of any woman as a love object becomes difficult.

Psychological impotence, homosexuality, and sexual perversion have somewhat similar roots and create somewhat similar problems in marriage. All apparently trace back to prior experiences by which the victim develops harmful emotional linkages with sexual expression and caress, with himself in the appropriate sexual role, or with a person of the opposite sex as an apt love object.

Emotional association is not a logical thing. For instance, one day I was driving along the railroad track with my small children in the back seat. My wife had just pointed out the train running beside us, and the youngsters were gazing at it in amazement. Suddenly the train blew its whistle loudly, and at exactly the same moment I had to jam on the brakes to avoid collision with a truck. The children tumbled frightened and bruised into the foot well of the car. For weeks afterward, the distant sound of a train whistle would make them cry—yet neither the train nor its whistle had any real connection with their discomfiture.

It is the same way with crossed wires in the sexual sphere. Ideas and emotions link because they happen at the same time, or become linked with all women when they apply only to one, or because the same words are used for shameful as for perfectly proper things. You cannot talk yourself out of these notions, because they are too illogical for argument. Perhaps you can gradually overcome them by favorable experience—my children finally heard enough train whistles without further harm that their hangup disappeared—but sexual and interpersonal relations involve so many vicious circles and downward spirals that this often does not work. A man who fails in an early attempt at intercourse loses confidence, bestirs reactions in his partner, and jeopardizes his reputation for manliness. A person may or may not have enough emotional aberration to harm his potency when he starts homosexual practices, but the resulting sexual self-doubt and emotional associations certainly add to the difficulty. Even sexual practices or urges which are entirely normal, like masturbation or mouth-to-genital play, may through misinformation become sources of guilt, uncertainty, and anxiety.

Anyone with a perversion (or substantial concern about perversion) should see a psychiatrist. "Perversion" in this sense means a *preference for other forms of sexual fulfillment when climax through intercourse is readily available.*

This definition is as important for what it *excludes* as for what it *includes.*

Nothing you do or feel inclined to do as a preliminary to intercourse is a perversion. Again, mouth-to-genital play as a preliminary to intercourse does not signify perversion.

Nothing you do or feel inclined to do as a "better than nothing" alternative when man-woman intercourse is unavailable constitutes perversion. Masturbation, for instance, is not a perversion unless actually preferred over sexual relations in an acceptable framework. It is perfectly normal for some husbands to masturbate occasionally, even while living with their wives. If the husband's sex pace is more active than his wife's and if the extra turmoil necessary to "get all he needs" in bed doesn't seem worthwhile, masturbation may seem the best choice available. Similarly, sexual release with a member of your own sex does not necessarily make you a pervert if circumstances or social restraints close off the man-woman avenue. Prisoners who get sexual release from their cellmates may have no homosexual leanings whatever when heterosexual release is available.

One couple I know were very much concerned about the husband's normality because on one occasion when the wife was menstruating—their particular backgrounds led them to regard menstruation as prohibiting normal intercourse—the husband proposed sexual use of the rectum. Such impulses (or even practices, the partner being willing) do not constitute a perversion when viewed as second bests or last resorts, even though they would fall into that category if actually preferred to intercourse.

Perhaps, in the existing framework of strongly anti-homosexual values, you might want to give perversion an extra wide margin. I have seen many marriages wrecked by aftermaths of practices which were actually normal, but which (through misapprehension or misunderstanding) stirred guilt in the "offender" or revulsion in the partner. On the other hand, you cannot let ignorance (either your own, your partner's, or your community's) put your sex life in a straightjacket. If experimentation, special urges, or unusual needs ever draw you close enough to perversion that you become concerned about the situation, read the definition and explanations above very carefully. If you have any further question about the matter, talk it over with a trained expert. It's better to settle these issues promptly than to let them rankle, especially since there are a dozen or more false alarms for every genuine fire.

"There's just no feeling at all," Phyllis Sloan said. "It's like I was made of wood. My organs aren't numb or anything, and I seem to have normal feeling the rest of the time. But when my father—I mean my husband—has intercourse, I literally don't feel a thing."

"You mean not only no excitement but not even a sensation of touch?"

"That's right. Just as if I'd been shot full of novocaine or something."

Even though Phyllis had pretty well figured out that her trouble was in her mind instead of her body, a physical examination seemed in order. After it was over and I had assured her that she had no signs of physical disease, Phyllis said:

"But it seems an awfully funny time to get frigid. I'm

forty-one years old, you know. And I've always gotten along pretty well with John sexually. We didn't finish together *every* time, but often enough. Why am I completely frigid now?"

"You're not. When you get no feeling in the organs at all, that's a different problem from frigidity. It's sexual anesthesia, and it's almost always based on muddled feelings about sex and the sexual relationship or about your relationship with this particular man."

"But I don't feel upset—I don't feel *anything*."

"That's because the mind blanks out all feeling to protect itself from some forms of emotional turmoil. Maybe the best way to explain how it works is to tell you about a different case. You'll know how long ago it happened when I tell you that cars in those days almost all had a gear shift level on the floor, and that lots of girls were still very prim and modest. The patient was particularly prudish, a Methodist minister's daughter reared under the strictest of moral rules. She went on a date one night, and woke up the next morning unable to move her left leg. She did not feel touch from the hip down, she had no reflexes in the ankle or the knee, and she didn't even twitch a toe when you jammed a needle into it.

"Fortunately, she saw a very knowledgeable doctor right away, and he was able (with the aid of drugs) to draw out the whole story. Her date was with a handsome lad for whom she had some yearning, and both of them were somewhat flustered and fumbling on this first big night. In fact he was so flustered that, completely by accident, his hand slipped off the knob while he was shifting into third, and ran all the way up the inside of her thigh. For a brief moment, she felt almost overwhelmed. Then the moment was over. For the rest of the evening, they were both tense and distant, and he made nothing approaching an indecent advance. But in the morning her leg was like a thing apart.

"What had happened? The irresistible force met the immovable object. Instead of feeling shocked or affronted when the boy's hand ran up her thigh, the girl had a keenly pleasurable physical response that ran smack up against the code she was raised on—the idea that fleshly pleasures were bad, sexual response in a woman was looseness, erotic sensation a thing of the Devil and wrong, wrong, wrong.

"That's what a psychiatrist means when he talks about 'conflict'—not conflict between people, between the boyfriend wanting to pet and the young lady resisting, but conflict between two strong forces within your own personality: an urge or desire that runs counter to a moral conviction, a pleasurable response to something your conscience says you should abhor, a feeling of hatred toward someone whom you feel you owe total love. Such conflict is unbearable to the mind. It has to be resolved or dodged or tempered in one way or the other, and this particular patient chose a very simple way: She cast her left leg into limbo rather than admit that any thigh which squirmed with pleasure at the touch of a handsome young lad's hand could possibly be a part of *her*.

"That was the story, and when she had told it the girl could move her leg. Once she had actually faced the issue, turned over its pros and cons in her conscious mind, the conflict was resolved in another way. Rejection of the whole limb no longer seemed worthwhile. But if the situation had not been handled promptly and well, that girl might be a cripple still.

"A pattern like this starts because of conflict at a fundamental level which is too painful at the time for you to face by yourself. Your mind quickly obscures even the memories of such an incident to protect itself from the unbearable turmoil of unresolved conflict. A psychiatrist can help by giving you the feeling that you are not alone in facing your problems, and by guiding your thoughts slowly and tortuously—despite your mind's attempts to avoid the issue—back toward the key experience. Once you relive it in conversation and conscious thought and see how basically illogical such a way of handling the matter is, it suddenly ceases to trouble you."

"You mean I can't stand the idea of sex with John? That if it gave me pleasure that would run smack into my moral code? I don't understand. We're married, and things were fine with us for twenty years."

"But suddenly they aren't fine anymore. Something happened, something changed in your viewpoint toward him, something altered your relationship. Now we've got to figure out what it was."

There is no reason for us to carry Phyllis Sloan's case further in full detail. We had many interviews before the full picture emerged. Just prior to the start of her trouble, she had learned that her husband was having an affair with his boss's secretary—exactly as her father had done when Phyllis was a child, with a resulting breakup of the family home. Phyllis constantly made "Freudian slips"—in talking about her husband she said "father" and vice versa— and clearly showed in many ways that she had come to confuse the two completely in her mind. Going to bed with her husband thus became equivalent to having intercourse with her father—not only incest but incest with the hateful cause of her family's breakup and misery. No wonder it was easier to live with no sexual sensation than with the guilt and anger these crossed wires engendered!

At last word, after months of gradually increasing insight into the emotion-taboo-mixed-identity turmoil involved in her problem, Phyllis seemed substantially better. An illness of this type always proves stubborn, though, once it is thoroughly intrenched. And it is no place for amateurs or for self-help. If you ever encounter sexual anesthesia on emotional grounds, prompt care by a psychiatrist is your best bet. Forced "cures" by hypnosis or overly abrupt discourse can deprive the victim of the protection her symptoms are giving against intense conflict without letting her resolve the issue, and serious depression, schizophrenia, or other totally disabling mental illnesses can sometimes result.

Of course, not all victims of the type of conflict which plagued Phyllis have illnesses grave enough to call for psychiatric care. "Love at first sight," for example, often stems from similarities in manner or approach (not usually in appearance) between the person who attracts you and a parent or other former love object. If you were imbued with taboos against incest in a poorly defined way, intercourse with a partner whom you link in your mind with your father or mother may stir guilt and conflict. People who find an autumn-spring marriage disgusting usually have incest-limiting taboos so strong and so broadly defined that any father-figure bed play seems deeply wrong. Their own sex life frequently suffers, especially if there is any age difference at all in their own marriage. Full discussion of this matter, even when it *seems* unrelated to sexual difficulties, often proves a real help.

"Wasn't there some character in fiction who always wound the clock every Sunday night, then went upstairs and had sexual intercourse?" Zelda Noonan asked.

"Tristram Shandy's father," I said.

"Well, it should have been Mike. Only it's Tuesday and

Friday with him, regular as a clock. If he had a flat tire on the way home from the bowling alley on Tuesday he'd have to masturbate before he could take time to fix it."

"Oh come on now!" Mike exclaimed. "I want it twice a week. Everybody says that's a normal sex pace. Why try to make me look ridiculous?"

"Because I'm tired of doing it that way! There's no spontaneity, no romance, not even any doubt. Tuesday or Friday, roll over and take your medicine!"

"So that's the way I am. Why change it?"

"I suppose you're the same way in other things," I said. "And maybe it has its advantages. You're an engineer, I see. You wouldn't be much good if you didn't insist on everything being just right. And you're very neat in appearance. I'll bet you keep your clothes just so."

"So damn neat I can't get near them," Zelda said. "Everything has got to be just so—clothes, tools, every book on the shelf, and of course sex by the numbers: hup, two, three."

"All right! All right!" Mike exclaimed intensely. "I've got to do things the way they're meant to be!"

"And in sex that's twice a week," I said.

"Isn't it?"

I shrugged. "There's a tremendous range for normal sex pace," I said, "from a few times a year to over a thousand. And mood plays a big part in the sex urge. Most couples have intercourse much more often on a vacation than they do back home, for instance. I usually regard any sex pace that both partners can comfortably live with as being normal no matter how the numbers come out. There's no reason to think of yourself as abnormal if your pattern falls outside the usual range. Besides, the usual range is broad enough to include twice a month as well as twice a week."

"But what's normal for us?" Mike asked. "And how can we get things set up to take care of it?"

Mike really didn't get the point that day, or any other day as far as I know. He couldn't solve a problem by give-and-take—only by setting a different routine. I sent him to a psychoanalyst who worked with him for a few months, but Mike stayed pretty much the same. Zelda, who was not very yielding either and couldn't do things *his* way, finally divorced him.

Mike's inflexible sexual routines were part of a rigidly structured living pattern. Rigid routines have their advantages, of course. Besides helping with some lines of work, they let you handle routine chores without wasted mental and physical effort. If you always put your socks in the same drawer, you never have to hunt for them. But you get harm instead of good out of carrying routines too far. When you need your socks not only in the same drawer but sorted by color in precise spectral sequence (as Mike did) , you spend much more time sorting and arranging than you would picking out the pair you want to wear. And when routine takes over personal functions in which there should be a large emotional element—when your behavior toward a friend, a husband or wife, or one of your youngsters is governed totally by rules and rituals instead of allowing for give-and-take interplay—your relationships suffer.

Ideally, sex is part of an intimate personal relationship. If any deep-seated element in your personality interferes drastically with your intimate relations or with the sexual expression of them, psychotherapy probably offers your best hope. Self-help simply doesn't work in this situation. Your mind veers off from reviving conflicts which were too painful for you to deal with as they came along. Occasionally you can build bridges—start from the areas of your personality strength, nurture good relationships, build self-confidence, develop trust and learn to communicate until you blossom as an intimacy-capable personality without formal aid. But you can never eliminate deep-seated inhibitions, aversions, and difficulties by thinking back to the source of such troubles. You need the interested concern and guidance of a trained professional. Your religious advisor or a social worker, psychologist, or psychiatrist may be of help. If they cannot work with you themselves, these people usually know whom you should see.

In my experience, however, at least half of the difficulties which make sex a problem instead of a blessing can be corrected by better sex techniques, nutrition, birth control, choice of medications, or other simple and definitive means. Another substantial portion clear up through better understanding of the male and female roles in marriage and through improved communications. Still more stem from inhibitions, such as excessive modesty, which usually disappear when you challenge them or think them through. All of these difficulties are subject to attack right at home, without professional aid. Hopefully the insights you have gained through reading this book will help you with any problems of this sort, as well as improving your understanding of other people. If you understand sex, you understand and increase your capacity for intimacy. And if you fulfill your role better in the spheres of intimacy a whole new life opens up.

Index

Adequacy, Sexual, 13–14
Affairs, Extramarital, 121
Age and sex, 74
Alcohol, 77, 80
Action path, 49
Amphetamines, 77
Angle of entry, 50
Arguments, 1
Assertiveness, 65
Association, Emotional, 63
Attitudes, xi
Attractiveness, Fading, 111–12
Averages, 5
Aversion, Pill-related, 91

Benzedrine, 77
Birth control, 91
Blame fixing, 2
Blood pressure pills, 77
Blood sugar, 78
Breast play, 21–22

Caress
    General, 21–22
    Male genitals, 27
    "Snake bite," 31
Case reports, xiv–xv
Catholic doctrine, 110–11
Cervix, 106
Child-bearing effects, 114

Climax
    Fast, 16
    Male, 17
    Multiple, 19–20
    See also Orgasm
Clitorine orgasm, 46
Clitoris, 20, 24–25
    Placement of, 47
    Retraction of, 22
Communication about sex, xii
Compromise, xii
Coldness, see Frigidity
Competitiveness, 3
Compulsive sex, 164
Conditioned reflex, 49
Conflict, 161
Conscience, 134
Considerateness, 67
Contract marriage, 33
Cunnilingus, 158
Creeping sensations, 111
Cyst of verumontanum, 17
Cystocele, 114–15

Demonstration, Sexual, xiii–xiv
Depression, 87–88
Desire, 98
Dexedrine, 77
Diabetes, 78
Diaphragm, 92
Dichotomies, 141
Difficulties, Sexual, xi

Dirtiness of sex organs, 23, 41
Divorce, 127–28
Drive, Competitive, 3

Ejaculation, Premature, 16
Electric treatment, 119
Emotional association, 63, 157
Entry Angle, 50
Equality of sexes, 39, 60
Erection, 76
  Faulty, 40
Excitement, Judging, 22
Exercises, 115–16
Expectations, 4
Experiments, xiii
Explanation of technique, xiii–
  xiv
Extramarital affairs, 121–33

Faked orgasm, 6, 33
Faithfulness *vs.* shopping, 38
Fear, 63
Fidelity, 38
Finger, 18
Foam, 92
Frenulum, 30
Fresh start, 7
Freud, 152
Frigidity, 58
  Passion-prostitute dichotomy,
    134
  Modesty and, 141–42
  Orgasm by play only, 44
  and the pill, 90
  vs. sexual anesthesia, 159–60
  Unrealistic expectations, 4
Front rim, 49

Generation gap, 152

Genital contours, 48
Genitals, Dirtiness, 23
Genitals, Male, 27–30
Guilt, 63

Hangups, 134–53, 157
Harmony of pace, 7
Hitting bottom, 106–107
Homosexuality, 156, 158
  Fear of, 103
Honeymoon, 3–4, 138
  Sexologic, 7
  Wife's response during, 65
Hormones, 91
Hot flashes, 111
Husband's rights, 35
Hymen, 139
Hysterectomy, 105
Hysteria, 159–60

Identity conflicts, 154–66
Impotence, 74–89
  Depression and, 87–88
  Hangups and, 88–89
  Premarital, 40
  Psychogenic, 154
  Sex technique and, 85
Incest, 162
Infidelity, 121–33
Inhibitions, Common, 134–53
Injury, Genital, 109–110
Inner lips, 23
Insults, 1
Intimacy, 165–66

Labia (lips), 23–24
Love, 33–43
  Definition, 68

Lubrication
   Artificial, 118–19
   Natural, 24

Madonna-prostitute dichotomy, 141
Male menopause, 75
Marriage as contract, 33
Masters and Johnson, 47
Masturbation, 72
Masturbation equivalent, 124
Masturbation, Feminine, 26
Medicines, 77
Menopause, Male, 75
Menopause, Sex and, 105–120
Metabolic impotence, 78
Modesty, 61–62, 141–42
Mouth-to-genital play, 157–58
Muscles, Genital, 115–16
Muscle relaxants, 81

Neurosis, 152
Nudists, 20
Nudity, 144
Nutrition and potency, 78

Obsession, 163–64
Oldness, 74
Operation, Need for, 114–15
Orgasm
   By Play only, 44–57
   Clitoral, 46
   Fake, 6
   Frequency in female, 5
   Multiple, 20, 56
   Simultaneous, 4, 11
   Vaginal, 46

Ovaries, 107, 111
Overachievers, 3

Pace, Disharmonious, 7, 99–100, 134
Passion-prostitute dichotomy, 141
Pavlov, 49
Penis
   Angle of entry, 50
   Caress of, 27–28
   Size of, 26, 106
   Tip, Sensitivity of, 28–29
Perversion, 23, 86, 157–58
Petting, 18
Pill, 90–104
Play, 16–32, 85–86
Play-only orgasm, 44–57
Position, Sexual, 50
   Inverted, 52–53
   Vagina snugging, 117–18
Potency fears, 74–89
Precoital play, 16–32
Prediabetic curve, 77–78
Pregnancy fears, 105
Pregnancy, Sex-restoring exercises, 118
Premarital sex, 33
Premature ejaculation, 16
Preparation, 16–32
Privacy, 146
Progesterone, 91
Prolaspe, 114–15
Promiscuity, 38
Prostate, 77
Prostatitis, 17
Prostitute-or-impassioned, 135
Psychiatrist, 161

Queers, 86

Rape, 109
Rectocele, 114–15
Rehabilitation, 2, 7
Reports, Case, xiv
Reproduction as proof of
    womanhood, 109–110
Responsiveness, Feminine, 11
Results, xiv
Retracted clitoris, 22
Rights, Husband's, 35
Romance, 43

Scorekeeping, 10
Secrecy, xv
Sedatives, 77
Self-doubt, 9–10
Sex
    After surgery, 106
    As commodity, 33–34
    As super-caress, 63
Sex aversion, 90
Sex life, control of, 38–39
Sex, Rightness of, 110
Sex organs, Dirtiness of, 23, 41
Sexes, Equality, 60
Sexual anesthesia, 160
Sexual scorekeeping, 10
Shame, 63
Shopping around, 38
Simultaneous orgasm, 4, 11
Size of penis, 26, 106
Sleeping pills, 77
"Snake bite" caress, 31
Snug-up surgery, 114–15
Sodomy, 158–59
Squabbles, 1

Stimulants, 77
Straining, 117
Striving, 3
Sugar in blood, 77–78
Surgery, Vaginal, 114–15

Technique, 18
    For older couples, 87
Tranquilizers, 77
Trigger, Male, 19

Understanding, xii
Uterus, Prolapse of, 114–15
Urethra
    Female, 26–27
    Male, 29

Vacations, 145–46
Vagina, 41
    Contours of, 48–49
    Dirtiness of, 23
    Relaxed, 114
    Short, 106–107
Vaginal orgasm, 46
Vaginismus, 109
Values, xii–xiii
Verumontanum, Cyst of, 17
Viewpoints, Rehabilitation, 22
Vitamins, 78–79

Weight control pills, 77
Womanhood, 109
Worth, Woman's, 60, 152

THIS BOOK WAS SET IN

BASKERVILLE AND BODONI BOLD TYPES BY

MARYLAND LINOTYPE COMPOSITION COMPANY.

IT WAS PRINTED AND BOUND BY

THE HADDON CRAFTSMEN, INC.

DESIGNED BY JOEL SCHICK